MEASURING AND GAGING IN THE MACHINE SHOP

developed by
National Tooling and Machining Association

1357 Rockside Road
Cleveland, OH 44134
800.248.6862
www.ntma.org

PREFACE

The National Tooling & Machining Association has answered the requests repeatedly voiced by schools and industry for a basic textbook on metrology for the machine shop. *Measuring and Gaging in the Machine Shop* is intended to introduce the tools of metrology to students in machining trades programs.

The instruments and concepts of measurement are basic knowledge acquired by journeymen tool and die makers, moldmakers and precision machinists, and become second nature as skills of the trade. The intent of this text is to help the student recognize which instruments provide the speed and accuracy needed to perform a given measuring task. Skill will develop through experience in a machine shop atmosphere. NTMA's compression-of-experience technique enables the student to become self-confident and productive as quickly as possible.

Measuring and Gaging in the Machine Shop is written for secondary, post-secondary and apprentice level student programs with emphasis on machine shop terminology and practical applications.

TABLE OF CONTENTS

"When you can measure what you are speaking about and express it in numbers, you know something about it; and when you cannot measure it, when you cannot express it in numbers, your knowledge is of a meagre and unsatisfactory kind. It may be the beginning of knowledge, but you have scarcely in your thought advanced to the stage of a science."

LORD KELVIN

Chapter I

Measurement: The Language of Precision

WHAT IS MEASUREMENT?

Measurement is the process of finding out how many measuring units there are in something by comparing it to a predetermined standard. Measurement provides answers to an almost endless list of questions such as: How many? How long? How high? How much? How deep? How heavy? How fast? The only way to obtain this information accurately is to take readings on various kinds of measuring instruments, and then interpret the readings.

Every measurement involves two things: (1) a number and (2) a unit of measure recognized as a standard. A number, by itself, is not a measurement. No one would know what you are talking about if you describe a piece of stock as having a length of 6. Do you mean 6 inches, 6 feet, 6 centimeters or 6 meters? But if you described the stock as being 6 inches long, then everyone knows what you mean. Therefore, a *unit* of measurement is a quantity adopted as the standard by which any other quantity *of the same kind* is measured. Many units of measure can be related in certain specific ways. Linking these related units together gives us *systems of measurement.*

HISTORICAL DEVELOPMENT OF MEASUREMENT

The modern level of technology that has made possible our present standard of living could not have been attained without the development and use of standardized measuring devices. Every advance in technology—from the earliest times—was preceded by the development of instruments that enabled man to see, measure, and gain access to the unknown he was probing. Man, himself, has incredibly sensitive and powerful measuring instruments within his own body: his senses of sight, sound, touch, smell, and taste. The same scientific principles involved in the use of man's own senses are employed in the measuring instruments and gaging devices used in his technological environment.

It is believed that human body measurements served as the standards for early measurements of length, whereas early weight standards were derived from the use of certain containers, or calculations of how much weight a man or beast could lift or haul. In any case, the standard units of weights and measures of the ancient empires of the Near and Middle East gradually found their way West—mostly as a result of trade—to the Greek and then the Roman empires, then on to Central Europe and Britain via Roman conquest.

Although it is thought that many very early civilizations devised standards of measurement and some measuring tools, the Egyptian *cubit* is generally recognized as the most widespread standard of linear measurement in the ancient world. Devised about 3000 BC, it was based on the length of a man's arm from his elbow to the tip of his extended fingers (see Fig. 1-1). It was standardized by a royal master cubit made from black granite and kept at Giza, against which all the cubit sticks in Egypt were measured at regular intervals.

In the first thousand years BC, commercial domination of the Mediterranean passed into the hands of, first, the Greeks and then the Romans. A basic Greek standard unit of length was the *finger*, 16 fingers equalled one foot, and 24 fingers equalled one Olympic cubit.

The Romans, adapting the Greek system, subdivided the foot into 12 inches (*unciae*), using the same word and the same subdivision for one-twelfth of a pound. They made five feet equal to one pace (or double step), a thousand of which made up the Roman mile.

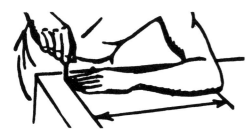

Fig. 1-1   *The cubit was one of the earliest standard units of length used by ancient peoples. The Egyptian pharoah's forearm was measured and established as the reference factor. In practice, it equaled the distance from a man's elbow to the tip of his finger.*

SYSTEMS OF MEASUREMENT

The English System

Out of the multitude of medieval weights and measures, several national metrology systems emerged, and were reformed and reorganized from time to time. Ultimately, nearly all of these European systems were replaced by the metric system. However, in England and its American colonies, the ancient systems survived, and were standardized by either royal ordinance or parliamentary law in the 1300s. However in 1965, England began an official changeover to metric measurement, leaving the United States alone to cope with the vestiges of the ancient methods.

The two major systems of measurement used in manufacturing in the United States today are the U.S. customary and the SI metric. The measurement units of each system can be converted to the other.

U. S. Customary

The U.S. customary system is a modified version of the English system passed on to us by "Mother England" during our colonial days. The common units of measure for length are the inch, foot, yard, and mile. The inch (in.) is divided into smaller parts, or fractions, for finer measurements. One method of division results in the *common fractions:* 1/2 in., 1/4 in., 1/8 in., 1/16 in., 1/32 in., and 1/64 in. As you know, the inch is also divided by another method into *decimal fractions*, such as 1/10 in., 1/100 in., or 1/1000 in. In most machine shop work—and especially on engineering drawings of parts that will be precision-machined—decimal fractions are expressed in decimal form, such as 0.1 in., 0.01 in., and 0.001 in., etc. A table of common fractions from 1/64 in. to 20 in. and their decimal equivalents that you can use for reference is given in the Appendix. Frequently used fraction-decimal equivalents should be memorized.

When dealing with measurements in the inch system, machinists and toolmaker's "shoptalk" most often refers to decimal parts of the inch in terms of "thousandths." Thus, although 0.100 in. is actually 1/10 in., we refer to it as "a hundred thousandths." Because "thousandths" is a difficult word to pronounce properly, the word is often shortened in conversation to "thou." If you hear someone say "fifty thou" in the shop, they mean 0.050 in.

One ten-thousandth of an inch (0.0001 in.) is often referred to as a "tenth." "Half a tenth" means 0.00005 in. If someone refers to a "tenth," remember that this means 0.0001 in. in shop talk, not 0.1 in.

SI Metric System

The SI metric system is now the international system of measurement used by about 95% of the people on Earth. For ease of international commerce, the metric system is gradually being adopted by the United States. As a machinist or toolmaker involved in producing goods shipped in international commerce, you must have an understanding of this system of measurement.

The base SI unit for length is the meter (m). The common multiples and sub-multiples for length in the metric system are the millimeter, centimeter, decimeter, meter, and kilometer as

10^{-3} meter	=	a *milli*meter	(mm)	.001
10^{-2} meter	=	a *centi*meter	(cm)	.01
10^{-1} meter	=	a *deci*meter	(dm)	.1
10^{0} meter	=	a meter	(m)	1
10^{1} meters	=	a *deka*meter	(da)	10
10^{2} meters	=	a *hecto*meter	(ha)	100
10^{3} meters	=	a *kilo*meter	(km)	1000

Fig. 1-2 Sub-multiples and multiples of the meter.

shown in Fig. 1-2. The multiples and sub-multiples reflect the powers of 10. Because metric units are based upon the decimal system of counting or multiples of 10, the multiples or sub-multiples of any unit are related to the unit by powers of 10.

As shown in Fig. 1-3, sets of multiples and sub-multiples composed of ones, tens, and hundreds are grouped into "periods" of three digits, separated by a space (instead of a comma as in the inch system) or a decimal point. Ones can occupy both the first and last position in a set of three digits. Tens are always in the second position, and hundreds are always in the third position. Therefore, whether you read from left to right or right to left from a space or decimal point, the digit that is one place over is a multiple or sub-multiple of 1, the digit two places over is a multiple or sub-multiple of 10, and the digit three places over is a multiple or sub-multiple of 100, etc.

Just as inch dimensions are described on drawings as so many "thousandths" and "tenths" without actually adding the word "inches," the equivalent range of millimeter dimensions are described as "tenths" or "hundredths" without adding the word "millimeters."

Numerical Magnitude			**Powers of 10**
1 000 000 000 000	=		10^{12}
1 000 000 000	=		10^{9}
1 000 000	=		10^{6}
1 000	=		10^{3}
100	=		10^{2}
10	=		10^{1}
0.1	=		10^{-1}
0.01	=		10^{-2}
0.001	=		10^{-3}
0.000 001	=		10^{-6}
0.000 000 001	=		10^{-9}
0.000 000 000 001	=		10^{-12}

Fig. 1-3 How to read multiples and sub-multiples of metric units.

1 kilometer	= 0.6214 mile
1 meter	= 39.37 inches
1 meter	= 3.2808 feet
1 meter	= 1.0936 yards
1 centimeter	= 0.3937 inch
1 millimeter	= 0.03937 inch
1 micrometer (μm) (0.001 millimeter)	= 0.00004 inch
also called a micron	
1 mile	= 1.609 kilometers
1 yard	= 0.9144 meter
1 foot	= 0.3048 meter
1 foot	= 304.8 millimeters
1 inch	= 2.54 centimeters
1 inch	= 25.4 millimeters
1 microinch	= 0.025 μm

Fig. 1-4 Metric and customary conversions for linear measure.

You will sometimes need to convert measurements from the customary system to the metric system, or vice versa. Although you can calculate the conversions mathematically using the conversions given in Fig. 1-4, a conversion table (such as the one given in the Appendix) is sometimes more convenient to use.

The metric system of measurement was gradually developed in France during the 1700's and by 1875 it had been recognized by most of the rest of the world including the United States.

The principal features of the new system were the convenience of having multiples and sub-multiples of units based on factors of *ten,* and having a true *system* of measurement structured upon a handful of *base* units of measure from which other units could be derived.

In 1960, the metric system was further modernized to reflect the demands of the 20th century. The modernized metric system of measurement now recognized throughout the world is known as SI Metric (for "Systeme Internationale" or "international system").

In 1976, Congress passed an act calling for voluntary conversion to the metric system of measurement in the United States. Metric usage is slowly but steadily growing and toolmakers and machinists must be familiar with metric measurements as well as with U. S. customary units.

QUALITY CONTROL

The application of the principles of mass production has led to major improvements in product uniformity and quality through the years, by means of ever-increasing dimensional control. Product quality requires accuracy in manufacturing operations which, in turn, demands that close tolerances be maintained to turn out parts that are interchangeable and give the best operating service. As you know, for mass production to be successful, any one of a large quantity of parts must fit together perfectly in an assembly. To maintain this degree of dimensional control, appropriate inspection techniques must be used to monitor and control production quality. The entire field of inspection is commonly known as *quality control.*

Very simply, the purpose of quality control is to make sure that manufacturing plans are carried out economically. This entails setting and checking production rates to determine if production volume is sufficient to meet demand, inspecting and testing to ensure that finished items conform to engineering specifications, and controlling costs to make sure that the product remains competitive.

To ensure that product specifications are met throughout the manufacture of a product, a formal or informal quality control program is established within the shop, which affects incoming purchased raw materials, production processes, and final acceptance of the product (final inspection) prior to packing and shipment to the customer. Quality control requires frequent inspections at various points in the production process to determine whether or not a product meets specifications in terms of appearance, dimensions, and overall operation.

Inspection

Inspection is the operation of comparing the actual condition of a workpiece to previously-chosen quality standards. This can involve checking workpiece dimensions with measuring instruments, or precision gaging to determine whether or not the workpiece is within the tolerances specified by the quality standard, which is usually the engineering drawing. Workpiece characteristics that are commonly inspected in the machine shop include: dimensional accuracy, accuracy of position and alignment, angular relationship, and accuracy of form.

The three main areas in a manufacturing operation in which inspection is carried out are:

(1) Receiving of incoming materials, (2) Production or in-process, and (3) Product acceptance or final inspection.

Receiving Inspection — Raw materials and components purchased from vendors in the form of individual parts, sub-assemblies, or assemblies are inspected for conformity to specifications or drawings before routing to storage, to production, or to assembly.

A receiving clerk may inspect incoming materials when the purchases consist of standardized articles. In this case, only a physical count and visual examination are necessary.

If the quantity or quality of purchased goods justifies it, the purchasing department may maintain its own inspection organization, or it may borrow inspectors from the inspection department as needed.

Production Inspection — The most efficient form of inspection during the production phase is in-process gaging or inspection that can be conducted without requiring additional handling simply for the sake of inspection. Such in-process inspections can range from simple manual measurements taken by the machinist or machine operator, to fairly complex gaging systems built directly into the production equipment.

Production inspection provides the opportunity to detect problems quickly and to make the necessary corrections before additional labor and material are wasted.

In some cases, it is desirable to inspect only one or two features of a part before going on to the next production operation. For example, when inspecting a cylindrical cast tubing in a production lot, before time is spent machining the inside diameter (ID) or outside diameter (OD); it is important to check both surfaces first to be certain that enough material is present to permit finishing of both the ID and the OD. A receiver (NOT-GO) hole gage could be used to check the OD of each piece before finishing the ID. If the casting is undersized, it can be rejected before time is wasted setting it up on the machine. If the parts are conveyorized, the gaging can often be done automatically.

Product Acceptance — Product acceptance or final acceptance involves inspection after a unit has been assembled. This inspection assures that the product functions properly, and has not been damaged during assembly. The finished units are selected at random as they come off the final assembly line, and subjected to service tests. Sometimes the product is disassembled, and each part is examined to determine the effect of the manufacturing operation. This procedure is a valuable aid in improving the design of parts and the quality of materials used in production.

Products that are sold on the basis of guaranteed performance are often installed and subjected to performance tests before shipment to the purchaser.

Statistical Quality Control

In high-production lots, it is impractical to inspect every characteristic and dimension of each part manufactured. However, research has shown that it *is* practical to employ the laws of probability in various ways to ensure acceptable product quality at a minimum of inspection cost and production delay. The random sampling of parts at certain points in the manufacturing cycle to inspect the critical part characteristics has proved highly successful in actual manufacturing practice. Years ago, trial and error indicated that a 10% sample was a reasonable starting point. Experience then dictated whether specific inspections needed to be increased or decreased.

More recently, however, the sampling process has become much more sophisticated. The

Single sampling plans for normal inspection (Source: Mil Std 105-D)

Sample size code letter	Sample size	0.010	0.015	0.025	0.040	0.065	0.10	0.15	0.25	0.40	0.65	1.0	1.5	2.5	4.0	6.5	10	15	25	40	65	100	150	250	400	650	1000
		Ac Re	Ac Re	Ac Re	Ac Re	Ac Re	Ac Re	Ac Re	Ac Re	Ac Re	Ac Re	Ac Re	Ac Re	Ac Re	Ac Re	Ac Re	Ac Re	Ac Re	Ac Re	Ac Re	Ac Re	Ac Re	Ac Re	Ac Re	Ac Re	Ac Re	Ac Re
A	2	▽	▽	▽	▽	▽	▽	▽	▽	▽	▽	▽	▽	▽	▽	▽	▽	0 1	1 2	2 3	3 4	5 6	7 8	10 11	14 15	21 22	30 31
B	3	▽	▽	▽	▽	▽	▽	▽	▽	▽	▽	▽	▽	▽	▽	▽	0 1	1 2	2 3	3 4	5 6	7 8	10 11	14 15	21 22	30 31	44 45
C	5	▽	▽	▽	▽	▽	▽	▽	▽	▽	▽	▽	▽	▽	▽	0 1	1 2	2 3	3 4	5 6	7 8	10 11	14 15	21 22	30 31	44 45	△
D	8	▽	▽	▽	▽	▽	▽	▽	▽	▽	▽	▽	▽	▽	0 1	1 2	2 3	3 4	5 6	7 8	10 11	14 15	21 22	△	△	△	△
E	13	▽	▽	▽	▽	▽	▽	▽	▽	▽	▽	▽	▽	0 1	1 2	2 3	3 4	5 6	7 8	10 11	14 15	21 22	△	△	△	△	△
F	20	▽	▽	▽	▽	▽	▽	▽	▽	▽	▽	▽	0 1	1 2	2 3	3 4	5 6	7 8	10 11	14 15	21 22	△	△	△	△	△	△
G	32	▽	▽	▽	▽	▽	▽	▽	▽	▽	▽	0 1	1 2	2 3	3 4	5 6	7 8	10 11	14 15	21 22	△	△	△	△	△	△	△
H	50	▽	▽	▽	▽	▽	▽	▽	▽	▽	0 1	1 2	2 3	3 4	5 6	7 8	10 11	14 15	21 22	△	△	△	△	△	△	△	△
J	80	▽	▽	▽	▽	▽	▽	▽	▽	0 1	1 2	2 3	3 4	5 6	7 8	10 11	14 15	21 22	△	△	△	△	△	△	△	△	△
K	125	▽	▽	▽	▽	▽	▽	▽	0 1	1 2	2 3	3 4	5 6	7 8	10 11	14 15	21 22	△	△	△	△	△	△	△	△	△	△
L	200	▽	▽	▽	▽	▽	▽	0 1	1 2	2 3	3 4	5 6	7 8	10 11	14 15	21 22	△	△	△	△	△	△	△	△	△	△	△
M	315	▽	▽	▽	▽	▽	0 1	1 2	2 3	3 4	5 6	7 8	10 11	14 15	21 22	△	△	△	△	△	△	△	△	△	△	△	△
N	500	▽	▽	▽	▽	0 1	1 2	2 3	3 4	5 6	7 8	10 11	14 15	21 22	△	△	△	△	△	△	△	△	△	△	△	△	△
P	800	▽	▽	▽	0 1	1 2	2 3	3 4	5 6	7 8	10 11	14 15	21 22	△	△	△	△	△	△	△	△	△	△	△	△	△	△
Q	1250	▽	▽	0 1	1 2	2 3	3 4	5 6	7 8	10 11	14 15	21 22	△	△	△	△	△	△	△	△	△	△	△	△	△	△	△
R	2000	▽	0 1	1 2	2 3	3 4	5 6	7 8	10 11	14 15	21 22	△	△	△	△	△	△	△	△	△	△	△	△	△	△	△	△

▽ = Use first sampling plan below arrow. If sample size equals or exceeds, lot or batch size, do 100 percent inspection.

△ = Use first sampling plan above arrow.

Ac = Acceptance number.

Re = Rejection number.

Fig. 1-5   *This table helps select sampling plans for various batch sizes at various acceptable quality levels (AQL). The AQL represents the number of defective parts that can be tolerated per hundred parts. The batch sizes are represented by the code letters running down the left side of the table (these are referenced in another table).*
For example, code letter "J" is for a lot of 501 to 1200 parts under normal inspection practices. Out of this batch, we would sample 80 parts, according to the table. If the AQL is 1.0, look down that column to the line corresponding to the sample size to find the acceptance number is 2 and the rejection number is 3. Hence, if three defects are found in the sample of 80, the entire batch would be rejected, whereas if only two defects were found among the sample, the batch would be acceptable.
These statistical techniques are most effective when numerous batches of the same products are used over relatively long periods of time.

mathematical application of the laws of probability to inspection sampling have resulted in sampling tables, which give the minimum inspection necessary for a particular lot size. The size of the sample derived from such a table depends upon the number of defective parts that management is willing to accept. The use of sampling tables is generally restricted to inspection of definite quantities of parts, such as lots, batches, or shipments. The statistical analysis takes the form of chart called a *histogram* on which the average size and the outer limits are quickly calculated for comparison with the specifications.

Whenever production is continuous, however, making batch sampling impractical, parts from the line are sampled periodically. A sample of 5, 10, or 15 parts is selected at specified time periods, such as every half hour or every hour. The samples are taken from those production points where critical dimensions or characteristics are being produced. By carefully inspecting a series of samples, it is possible not only to evaluate the quality of the product, but also to predict what will happen to the quality level during the next 1 to 2 hr. This is done by statistically analyzing and interpreting the data after they are incorporated into average and range charts. Comparing the two charts over a span of time can indicate such quality control factors as tool wear limits, need for machine tool adjustments, variations in material quality, etc.

Statistical quality control is frequently required in military defense-related batch production of precision machined parts. Sampling procedures governing such work are covered in Military Standard 105D, *"Sampling Procedures and Tables for Inspection by Attributes."*

The standard covers classification of defects, definitions of terms, acceptable quality levels, sampling plans, and considerations for normal, tightened, or reduced inspections. The standard also contains a series of tables such as the one shown in Fig. 1-5. Other tables in the standard cover such things as multiple sampling plans and reduced or tightened inspection routines.

To obtain a copy of Military Standard 105D or other "mil specs," as they are often called, write or call Publications Control Center, Navy Supply Depot (DCI), 5801 Tabor Avenue, Philadelphia, PA. 19120. These standards are generally available free of charge upon request.

Quality control in manufacturing often requires frequent and careful inspection. The purpose of these inspections is not only to detect defective parts, but to identify the factors causing the defects so that they can be corrected. Quality checks and inspections are performed by different individuals at different types and sizes of manufacturing operations. Instead of a central inspection department, some shops use roving in-process inspectors. Others rely upon the production foreman or individual machinists within the production department to carry out inspection. Whoever performs the inspection procedures uses both measuring instruments and gages to compare the conformance of a part or product to the quality standard more closely than is possible by simple observation (see Fig. 1-6).

The Inspector's Judgment

Inspection is not purely a mechanical operation. Some items that are inspected will fall well inside the limits of the working standards; others will fall well outside those limits, and still others will fall close to the limits in either direction. In some cases, however, inspection results may be confusing, especially if the stated specifications are in error or incomplete. In such cases, the inspector must exercise good judgment. Resolving the problem may require a trouble-shooting process to determine exactly what the customer's requirements are.

It is obvious that if usable parts are rejected, manufacturing costs will be increased unnecessarily, and these costs must be reflected by either a higher selling price or a lower profit. On the other hand, if poor materials and workmanship are allowed to pass inspection, the finished product will not perform satisfactorily. Poor product performance will destroy a manufacturer's reputation for producing a quality article—a reputation built up over a number of years at great effort and expense in most instances—and the manufacturer will lose business to his competitors.

The disposition of rejected parts also calls for good judgement. Some must be scrapped, but others may be salvaged by corrective operations. The inspector may not be able to make such decisions alone, but may be able to make recommendations or suggestions as a member of a quality team. The inspector may also be able to identify recurring problems and recommend process improvements to reduce or eliminate nonconformities. Thus, you can see that the inspector's position is one of economic responsibility, as well as one of quality control.

STANDARDS OF MEASUREMENT

The very existence of units and systems of measurement implies the need for precise and uniform *standards*. When two people are talking about lengths or distances, they must be sure that both people are referring to an inch or centimeter that is of a particular standard length. If no standard inches or standard centimeters existed, any discussion involving these units would be meaningless.

Engineering metrology—in the modern sense—refers to the system of standardization and control that ensures accuracy and interchangeability of manufactured articles. This control must relate to national and international standards. Both the customary and the SI metric systems use the meter as the measurement standard for length. International scientists have defined the length of the international meter as 1,650,763.73

Fig. 1-6   *A machinist checking a part dimension after a machining operation.*

wavelengths of light from energized atoms of krypton-86. Even here in the U.S., the inch is legally and officially defined in terms of the international standard for the meter (1 inch = 0.0254 meters). Thus, everyday working standards can be constructed that are directly traceable to their fundamental SI definitions, and to the international meter definition. Physical standards based on this definition are prepared by use of extremely accurate laboratory equipment, and are maintained at the U.S. National Bureau of Standards, in national standards laboratories in various countries, and at the International Bureau of Weights and Measures in Sevres, France.

To maintain accuracy in a vast industrial complex such as the United States, standards must be traceable to a single source. The National Bureau of Standards is that source in the U.S. The Bureau maintains close connections with the International Bureau of Weights and Measures, thereby assuring that items manufactured to identical dimensions in different countries will be compatible.

Because precise measurement has so many applications, it is not practical for a single national laboratory to directly perform all the calibrations and standardizations required in a large industrially developed country such as ours. Therefore, standardizing laboratories have been established, both in industry and in various branches of the government. So that results of calibrations are uniform, the standardizing laboratories maintain close ties with the National Bureau of Standards, and use a uniform terminology in discussing standards.

Traceability and Calibration of Standards

The purpose of industrial laboratories is to assure that products are being fabricated according to standards based on the national standards maintained by the National Bureau of Standards.

The company or corporate standards are calibrated periodically at the National Bureau of Standards, the frequency of calibration depending upon the stability and wear resistance of the standard. The master gage blocks of the plant however, can be calibrated by the corporate laboratory itself. As a check on the accuracy of the corporate laboratory, an annual cross-test of

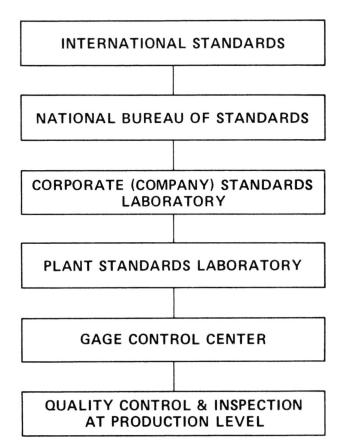

Fig. 1-7   Traceability and calibration of standards.

a small number of gage blocks, about 12, is made with the National Bureau of Standards.

Further, the corporate laboratory periodically compares the plant standards with their laboratory reference standards. In turn, each plant laboratory supports a gage control center, inspection groups, and production facilities by periodically comparing their measuring instruments and gages to the plant standards. In smaller single-plant companies, the functions of the corporate and plant laboratories are combined. The gage control center calibrates all special-design gages used by the production and inspection groups to check the product.

This kind of typical standards traceability and calibration system ensures that all references used to check or set instruments and gages for measuring the characteristics and features of the product are directly traceable to national standards through the several levels that make up the system.

The measuring equipment maintained by the plant laboratory will vary with the size, geometry, and precision requirements of the work to be inspected. The plant standards laboratory (or standards room, as it is sometimes called) must operate at the standard temperature of 20°C (68°F) and 35% to 45% humidity to maintain the proper environmental conditions for the working standards (See *Environmental Errors* on page 14) in the form of line standards and end standards.

Length Standards

Although length is the fundamental dimension in engineering metrology, the associated dimension of angle and the derived measurements of form, shape, and position are all important practical considerations in the manufacture of precision parts.

Length standards are available in several variations of three basic forms: line standards, end standards and light waves. Light wave methods are usually suited only to the laboratory.

Line Standards — These standards take the form of scales, usually ruled on steel bars or on glass, and may range in overall length from a fraction of an inch to several feet.

The steel bar standard is usually made from nickel steel alloy.

The surface of the bar is polished to a mirror reflection and the lines ruled on it have a uniform width throughout the length of the scale—usually within the range 0.0001 to 0.0003 in. The scale may be subdivided throughout its length as required, the most common sub-divisions being 0.01 in., 0.05 in., 0.2mm and 1mm.

Glass scales are mostly restricted to shorter lengths (20 in. and less), and the polished surface on which the lines are ruled is covered with glass for protection. The lines may be produced by (1) ruling through a resist, (2) etching with hydrofluoric acid and then filling, or (3) by evaporating a metal film onto the glass after ruling through a masking layer, after which the masking layer is removed chemically leaving the scale bonded to the glass.

End Standards — As their name implies, the form of these standards is such that their definitive length is their overall length from end to end. End standards are divided into two main groups: those having flat parallel end faces, and those having spherical end faces (see Fig. 1-8). Those

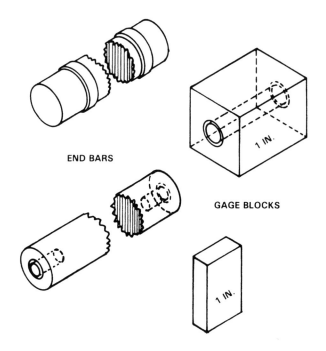

END BARS

GAGE BLOCKS

END STANDARD WITH SPHERICAL FACES

Fig. 1-8   Typical end standards.

having flat end faces, called *gage blocks* and *end bars*, are the more precise standards. End standards are usually made from steel, but chromium-plated steel, and tungsten and chromium carbides are also used to make gage blocks.

In gage blocks and end bars, the flat end faces are ground and then lapped to a very high degree of accuracy with regard to flatness, parallelism and their distance apart. The finish of these faces is extremely high—on the order of 1 microinch—and this characteristic, combined with their high degree of flatness, enables two or more gage blocks to be "wrung" together by first cleaning them and then bringing their faces into contact with a combined twisting and sliding motion. (You will learn more about using gage blocks shortly.) When wrung this way, the gages adhere strongly, and their combined length is the sum of their individual lengths.

The longer end standards and end bars are also produced to accuracies proportionally equivalent to those named above for gage blocks. Because of their slender form, you must take great care when using these longer standards on their horizontal axes to minimize the effects of deflections. As an aid, the positions along each standard at which it should be supported are often marked. In some cases, raised bands form an integral part of the bar at these positions (see Fig. 1-8). If the bar is properly supported at these positions, the end faces remain parallel.

In addition, when the longer end standards are joined together, another means of coupling must be added to the wringing film. This can take the form of loose studs in threaded holes in the ends of the bars, special clamps over the outer surfaces, or rods passing directly through the bars (see Fig. 1-8). It is essential, however, to make sure that the mating faces are properly "wrung."

The spherical-ended length standards cannot be used in combination. They are mainly used for special purposes, such as setting standards for large external micrometers. These standards are calibrated against flat-ended standards of higher quality, with proper allowance being made for any compression effects that may arise from the comparison technique used.

Angle Standards

Angular measurement is based on the subdivision of the circle. Therefore, any unit of angle is a geometrical concept, and is not derived from a natural or physical standard in the same way as the meter. However, three types of angle reference standards are in common use: (1) angle gage blocks, (2) precision polygons, and (3) circular scales. Circular scales are mainly incorporated in angular measuring instruments, such as rotary tables.

In the practical measurement of angles, two main systems of measurement are used: degree measurement and radian measurement. Degrees are usually subdivided into divisions of sixtieths or divisions of hundreds. In either, the basic quantity is the right angle. However, the system of degree measurement based on sixtieths is the most widely used. This system divides the circle into 360 equal parts or degrees and four right angles, and further subdivides the parts as:

1 right angle = 90° (degrees)
1 degree = 60′ (minutes)
1 minute = 60″ (seconds)

Angle Gage Blocks.   These are hardened steel blocks, stabilized to ensure dimensional stability, having two highly-finished measuring faces mutually inclined so as to form included angles of particular nominal sizes. The faces are flat to within a few millionths of an inch, can be wrung like gage blocks, and have a high degree of reflectivity. You will learn more about using angle gage blocks later in this course.

Individual angle gage blocks are manufactured to agree with their nominal size to within ±2 sec, and can be calibrated to an accuracy of ±1 sec. The calibration can be made without reference to any outside standard using a method called *size generation*. Size generation is closely linked with the initial manufacture of the blocks, and depends upon the production of three identical blocks for each nominal size produced. By exercising extreme care, all the angles can be brought to within ±1 sec of their nominal values. Once the master set has been produced, other sets can be calibrated by direct comparison with it, using a comparator of suitable design.

Precision Polygons — Precision polygons are blocks of regular polygonal form, made from steel, glass or fused quartz, which have reflecting peripheral faces. They are used to measure angular rotations, or to check the accuracy of angular measuring instruments. The most common polygon in use is one having an exterior angle of 30 deg, although polygons having exterior angles in the range of 5 to 72 deg are available. A polygon having 12 peripheral reflecting faces is shown in Fig. 1-9.

The reflecting peripheral faces of polygons are flat to a few millionths of an inch, square to the supporting base to ½ min, and possess a high

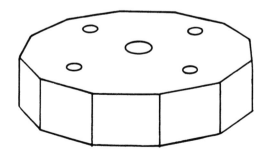

Fig. 1-9   A twelve-sided precision polygon.

degree of reflectivity. The faces of polygons constructed in glass or quartz are aluminized or treated by another means to increase their reflecting power. Steel polygons are stabilized to ensure dimensional stability.

An advantage in using the polygon for circular measurement is the fact that, when it is attached to an object being checked for accuracy of rotation, it is not necessary for the axis of the polygon to coincide precisely with the axis of rotation of the object. In other words, the alignment of the two axes of rotation is not critical. The angles of a polygon can be determined precisely by a method similar to that used to test the uniformity of a linearly-divided scale.

If you must check the accuracies of rotation of an angular measuring instrument at intervals closer than 5 deg (the limit of a single 72-sided polygon), you will have to use two or more polygons in combination. For example, a rotation could be checked at 1 deg intervals by using polygons having 72 and 40 sides, respectively. The 72-sided polygon would first be used to check every 5 deg interval with respect to the zero reading of the instrument. Four additional series of observations would then be required, beginning at the 1, 2, 3, and 4 deg readings, respectively. Each additional and independent series of observations is then related to the zero reading of the first series at eight points by using the 40-sided polygon to make observations at 9 deg intervals through a complete rotation, beginning at the zero reading. By adjusting the observations, you can achieve calibration at 1 deg intervals throughout.

Circular Scales — The standard of reference used in precise angular measuring instruments is usually a circular scale, engraved on glass or metal, mounted with its center on the axis of rotation of the instrument. This scale is viewed through a single microscope rigidly attached to the body of the instrument. Examples of instruments employing circular scales include circular dividing tables, dividing heads, theodolites, clinometers and protractors. The graduation lines of circular scales used in this class of measuring instrument can be correctly spaced to an accuracy of about 10 seconds. However, the accuracy of circular scales found in the shop is commonly 5 minutes (see Fig. 1-10).

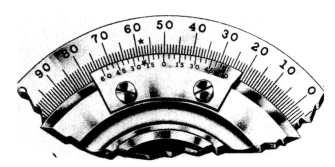

Fig. 1-10   The vernier portractor is a common type of circular scale. (Courtesy of The L. S. Starrett Company)

GAGES AND GAGE CONTROL

If measurement is the process of determining the dimension of a part by comparison with a standard unit of measure, what is gaging? *Gaging* is the process of determining whether or not a dimension of a part is larger or smaller than a predetermined standard or standards. To carry out their intended function successfully, gages must be made to a higher precision than the work they check and, therefore, their manufacturing tolerances are required to be relatively small. In addition, gages must be checked periodically by *check gages*, whose relation to the working gages is similar to that between working gages and parts. In other words, gages—and their check gages where appropriate—must each be checked by comparing them directly with standard gages or standards of a higher order. Therefore a complete system of gage control of parts in a manufacturing organization includes four steps, each of which usually represents an increase in accuracy: (1) part, (2) working gage, (3) inspection or check gage, and (4) master or standard gage.

Gage tolerance should be small compared with the corresponding part tolerance, and is usually taken as approximately 10% of tolerance. Working gages are used in the actual production of a part, whereas inspection gages are used in the subsequent verification of the part at final inspection. In the past, the limits for working and inspection gages were set so that all work passed by accurate working gages would also be passed by accurate inspection gages. Now, however, the tendency is to make only one type of gage, but in duplicate, and to assign the smaller gage to either working or inspection service, as appropriate. The gages are periodically inspected in use, and are interchanged if wear is found to be greater on the working gage than on the inspection gage. Sometimes, of course, the form of the working shop gage is different from that of the inspection gage, because of how the gage must be applied in production.

However, tolerances on inspection gages are generally smaller than those of the working gages they control. In principle, the inspection gage limits bear the same relationship to those of the working gages as the latter do to those of the part, but, due to the difficulty of manufacture, the tolerances for inspection gages often exceed 10% of those on the working gages. In fact, it is sometimes impracticable to use a complete system of "GO" and "NOT-GO" inspection gages when gage tolerances are small. (See examples in Chapter IV.)

For the machinist, efficient gage control includes:

(1) Periodic inspection of the gages that you use most frequently,

(2) Inspection of a gage by an authorized inspector before any job is started,

(3) Inspection of thread gages for thread form, lead, pitch diameter, major diameter, hardness, surface finish and thick-end threads (see Fig. 1-11),

(4) Inspection of thread ring gages by master setting gages, minor diameter plugs, and high-limit angle-check gages for thread form and surface finish,

(5) Inspection of plain cylindrical plug gages for size, out-of-roundness and taper, surface finish, and hardness,

(6) Inspection of snap gages for size and flatness of anvils, and

(7) Inspection of contour gages by a master template or by an optical comparator.

UNCERTAINTY IN PRACTICAL MEASUREMENTS

In all measuring and gaging operations in the shop, you are attempting to control, or compensate for, variables. *Variables* is simply the general name given to the features or characteristics you are measuring. All of these features and

Fig. 1-11   *The threads at one end of this gage will fit a nut of a certain specification; the threads at the other end will not fit. This is known as a GO/NOT-GO gage. (Courtesy of DoAll Company)*

characteristics are subject to variation and change; they may be greater or less or have different values under different conditions.

The variable in any measuring operation is the *dimension* or number of units of measurement you are seeking in the length, width, height, thickness, angle, or circumference of an object. All of these variables are directly related to the standards of length and angle that you learned about earlier in this chapter.

The variables in many gaging operations are the *geometric characteristics* of form and position. *Form* is the relative location of a group of points representative of the surface being measured. *Position* is the measurement of the location of a body with respect to a fixed coordinate system. Geometric variables are indirectly related to the standards of length and angle.

All of the raw materials used in manufacturing are derived from natural sources and, because of varying conditions, these basic raw materials also vary in both their chemical and physical characteristics. Further, the raw materials are processed by men who vary in their skills, and by machines, which are made by men and which introduce a new set of variables. This makes it impossible to machine parts to mathematically exact dimensions. Finally, more variables are introduced during measuring and gaging. The interaction of all these variables makes it virtually impossible to produce any two things that are exactly alike. Variability is the rule in manufacturing processes, not the exception.

In addition to the variables, there is the universal presence of uncertainty in physical measurements, because there are inherent errors in all measuring processes. Whatever system of measurement is used, the value of the number assigned to the result of the measurement to describe the magnitude of the variable will be in error to a greater or lesser extent. In other words, it will depart somewhat from the true value of the quantity. No measurement, however painstakingly carried out, or how often repeated, can ever completely eliminate this uncertainty. Thus, the true value of a measured physical quantity can never be stated with complete exactness. Therefore, one of the most important aspects of measurement is the attempt to restrict measurement errors to those limits that can be tolerated for the job at hand. This is the fundamental nature of tolerancing on shop prints and drawings—to adjust the basic dimensions slightly to accommodate the inevitable mechanical, measurement, and human error inherent in manufacturing any part or object. Tolerances specify the allowable amount of error (between decimal limits) that can exist and still permit the parts to function satisfactorily.

Errors are unavoidable in the comparison of an unknown with a reference standard, or in the calibration and use of a measuring system. The value of the reference standard itself is also uncertain by an amount that depends on the whole chain of measurements extending back to the national standards designed to maintain all measurements on a common basis. Measurement errors stem from five main sources: (1) systematic errors, (2) instrument errors, (3) calibration errors, (4) environmental errors, and (5) human errors.

Systematic Errors

Systematic errors are those consistently repeated each time the same measurement is made. They can be the result of: faulty calibration of the measuring system, a system malfunction that causes its indicator to depart consistently from the value assigned in calibration, aging of the elastic properties of a spring or diaphragm, or the reduced strength of a magnet through shock or aging. Because the user is unaware of the systematic errors, they are difficult to discover and trace to their cause.

If you suspect a systematic error, repeat the measurement using different instruments or, if possible, a different method of measurement. In this way, errors caused by incorrect instrument calibration, or that are inherent in a particular

method, should be evident. Sometimes you can measure an object of known magnitude to check the calibration of the measuring system. This will help to uncover any systematic errors that may be present.

Instrument Errors

Every measuring instrument has an inherent error of indication. This is because accuracy in the manufacture of measuring instruments affects the degree of accuracy of the reading. Like the parts you machine, the parts of measuring devices cannot be machined with absolute accuracy. These small inaccuracies result in one kind of instrument error, but they should be detected during routine examinations by the quality control inspectors.

Calibration Errors

Calibration is the process that determines an instrument's adherence to measurement standards. The calibration of all measuring devices begins with, and depends upon, the basic international and national standards of measurement that you learned about earlier in this chapter. Because you can't rush off to the National Bureau of Standards every time you need to measure a dimension, the National Bureau of Standards prepares and calibrates many practical standards for use by industry. Industrial firms, in turn, prepare and calibrate their own practical or working standards. Thus, there is a continuous chain of measurement standards that begins with the international standards, comes down through the national standards, and works all the way on down to the rules, gages, and other devices that you use every day to make measurements. In many firms, all instruments and devices are periodically cycled through the plant standards laboratory where they are calibrated against appropriate standards. There, any adjustments are made to bring the instruments into conformity with the standards. Only through this process can standardized measurements within an individual shop—or within an entire nation—be maintained.

However, because we know that all measurement is subject to a certain amount of error, the international and national physical standards also contain some error, even though it is almost unbelievably small. The error in the national reference standards, although extremely small, is somewhat greater than the error in the national standards, and when we get down to the actual measuring devices used in shop measurement, the error is larger still.

Environmental Errors

All matter is affected, to varying degrees, by its environment. This means that the properties of all materials are changed by temperature, pressure, humidity, radiation, and vibration.

Temperature difference is considered to be the greatest cause of error in measurements. Temperature variations affect the size and shape of metal parts, as well as the accuracy of the measuring instrument itself, which is also made from metal. Fig. 1-12 shows how various metals expand when room temperature is increased from 68° to 98°F.

For these reasons, calibration of instruments must be carried out in a special area (usually the standards laboratory) where the room temperature is maintained at a constant level of 68°F (20°C), the internationally-agreed-upon reference temperature for length measurements with variations of ±0.5°F, or less. Such enclosed areas (sometimes called *metrology laboratories*) also provide a continuous exchange of air in a uniformly-distributed flow, and at a rate that permits prompt correction of any temperature variations that may occur. The air introduced is filtered and dehumidified, with a relative humidity maintained at a level of 35 to 45%. The air pressure inside the room is kept slightly higher than that of the surrounding areas.

In addition, the lighting in these rooms must be uniform (almost shadowless), of sufficient intensity for delicate work, and arranged in a manner to reduce the effects of radiated heat. Although the location of a metrology or standards laboratory is always selected so as to reduce its exposure to vibrations, sometimes a separate foundation is built for the entire room.

Variations in environmental conditions will affect measurements taken in any location. Thus, even on the production floor, a reasonable degree of care should be taken to avoid any extreme variations and, particularly, any sudden changes in temperature. Remember that when you are measuring critical dimensions at high resolution, environmental variations—particularly in temperature—can affect the accuracy of the results you obtain.

Human Errors

Another major source of measurement error, especially when using handheld instruments, is caused by the human element. People create reading errors and errors of "feel" or "touch." Reading error is sometimes caused by a lack of skill. It is due to the uncertainty of the human eye in perceiving small intervals on a scale. One person may have no difficulty in determining which graduation marks line up on a vernier scale. Another, even with the aid of a magnifying glass, may not be able to determine which ones line up. This may be caused by lack of sufficient light with which to see the graduations clearly, and good lighting would tend to reduce the error. Reading errors may also be reduced by additional training and practice.

Remember that the line of measurement should coincide with the line of the rule or instrument. This is simply illustrated by measuring the separation of two parallel lines with a rule. If the rule is not placed exactly perpendicular to the lines, the true dimension will be the indicated value multiplied by the cosine of the angle of inclination—a "cosine" error.

A second type of human error is caused by individual differences in "feel" or "touch." Obtaining extremely accurate measurements with handheld instruments is an art. There are no indicating instruments to tell you when you have just the right feel. For example, when you measure

Metal	Expansion (linear inches per inch) from 68 to 98°F
Aluminum	0.0004
Brass	0.0003
Stainless Steel	0.00026
Steel	0.00018

Fig. 1-12   Metal expansion caused by temperature change.

a shaft with a micrometer, there is no gage to tell you when you have turned the thimble just the right amount. You must develop this feel through practice.

Much time can be lost if you are unsure of your judgment of the feel in reading instruments. If you are to turn a shaft to a tolerance of ±0.002 in., it is not practical to take the additional time necessary to machine the part to a tolerance of ±0.0002 in. You must develop the *feel* of working to practical limits.

By gaining experience with a variety of measuring instruments, and measuring a number of test pieces, you will learn to judge the right "feel" and repeat the reading obtained. Repeatability and "feel" are related to each other. The more you practice, the sooner you will develop your own ability to obtain an accurate measurement through "feel." Because there are many variables in measurement, chances for human as well as instrument error are always present.

The three basic human abilities used in accurate and repeatable measurements are: sight, touch, and judgment. You have each of these capabilities, but they need to be trained. The trained human eye can distinguish whether or not two lines match within 20 millionths of an inch (0.000020) under good conditions with a master vernier scale or master glass scale. Eyeglass lenses and other magnifying devices can make this discrimination even finer. With experience and training, some people can determine whether or not a certain dimension is within 0.005 in. or about $\frac{1}{3}$ of $\frac{1}{64}$ in., using a common 6 in. rule, but this is not normal practice.

Just as people are right- or left-handed, they also have a dominant eye. You can check this by lining up the end of your finger with a line in the room: If you close first one eye and then the other, you will find out which eye you should use to "sight" with. This is the eye that should be directly in line with the end of a part being measured. If it is not in line, you will create an error in the measurement.

Averaging of Repeated Measurements

Relying on a single measurement and instrument reading is always dangerous. The roughness or cleanliness of the contact surface, the accuracy of alignment of the workpiece and instrument, the degree of rigidity of the measuring setup, and potential human errors are all factors that can affect the accuracy of the reading. A good practice is to use the average of three readings. This does not mean that you simply read the instrument scale three times, but rather that you make three complete presentations of the part to the instrument. This can become time-consuming in surface plate setups. However, because surface plate setups have a high potential for errors, the implementation of this procedure assumes even greater importance.

Thus, you can improve the precision of a measurement and minimize reading errors by averaging a number of separate readings. The precision usually increases as the square root of the number of repetitions. You can obtain a similar improvement by allowing the instrument to average its measurement over a period of time during which the measuring variable remains constant.

MEASURING INSTRUMENTS VS. GAGES

Measuring and gaging are the vital links between the engineering drawings developed during product design and the precise configuration of the manufactured part or product. In product design, the parts of a product and their interrelationships are determined and specified on engineering drawings so that they become a working, unified whole. The specifications are part of the design standards in the form of dimensions, and usually include tolerances. Dimensions determine the length, width, and height of a part or detail.

For the machinist, measuring is the act of determining the dimension, or dimensions, of a part or object using a measuring instrument that allows the size of the dimension to be determined, either directly or indirectly, in units of measurement. Gaging, on the other hand, is the process of determining whether or not a dimension of a part is larger or smaller than the specified tolerances, or standards, by means of direct or indirect comparison. Therefore, the machinist uses both linear measuring instruments and comparison gages in controlling the dimensions of interchangeable parts.

Linear measuring instruments are classified into two types: direct-reading and indirect-reading. Direct-reading instruments contain a line-graduated

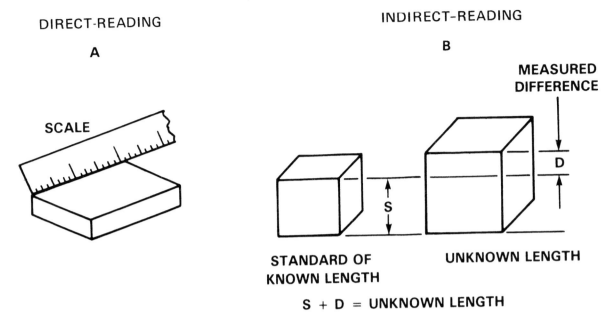

Fig. 1-13   Direct (A) and indirect (B) comparison measurements.

scale so that the size of the dimension being measured can be read directly upon this scale. Examples include the steel rule, micrometer, vernier gages, and optical comparator. Indirect-reading instruments do not contain line graduations themselves, but are used to transfer the size of the dimension being measured to a direct-reading scale, thereby obtaining the measurement indirectly.

Direct-reading measuring instruments are applied directly to the workpiece to obtain a measurement, as shown in Fig. 1-13A. Indirect-reading instruments, on the other hand, measure the *difference* between a known dimension and an unknown dimension or else transfer an unknown dimension to some other instrument. As shown in Fig. 1-13B the actual measurement of the unknown length is obtained by combining (either adding or subtracting) the measured difference and the standard of known length. Examples of indirect-reading instruments include the divider, caliper, surface gage with dial test indicator, sine bar, telescoping gage, and planer gage.

Gages are comparison-type measuring instruments used to measure both linear and angular dimensions during the production process. They are generally classified as either the fixed-type or the deviation-type. Fixed-type gages are designed to gage only one dimension to determine simply

whether or not the dimension is larger or smaller than a previously established standard. Deviation gages, on the other hand, indicate the amount by which a measured part deviates, plus or minus, from a standard to which the gage has been set. In most cases, such a deviation is indicated directly in units of measurement. In other cases, the gages show only whether or not the deviation is within a desired range. Nearly all deviation gages amplify the input signal so that very small deviations can be detected. Deviation gages are usually adjustable, which makes them useful in gaging a wide range of sizes. Dial indicators are the most common form of deviation gage.

It is actually impossible to separate measuring instruments from gages, and vice versa, because the two classifications overlap each other to a large extent. **A measuring instrument is any device that can be used to measure a linear, angular, or plane-surface dimension.**

However, in many manufacturing operations—particularly those involved with interchangeable parts—it is not necessary to measure parts to determine their exact size, but only to determine whether or not they are within tolerances. Further, the use of measuring instruments is relatively slow, and requires considerable skill if accurate measurements are to be obtained. Therefore, gages are the most widely-used devices for *controlling* linear dimensions during production and in inspection, for assuring interchangeability of the finished parts.

A gage determines the relative size or shape of the part by comparing the known dimensions of the gage to the unknown dimensions of the part. A gage may be a fixed-size or limit-type that simply accepts parts within tolerance and rejects parts outside tolerance (such as ring gages and plug gages), or an indicating type that actually measures the amount of deviation from a mean or basic dimension (such as micrometers, dial comparators, and pneumatic comparators).

Specific part conditions of size and form, and the positional relationships among various functioning surfaces require a machinist to use a wide variety of measuring and gaging instrumentation. Because any physical quantity may be measured by several different principles, and the measurement may be accomplished using various techniques and devices, no single method of distinguishing between, or classifying, measuring instruments and gages is possible.

For example, at one extreme, micrometers and vernier calipers are direct-reading measuring instruments. Either, however, may be set to a dimension and used to check work or adjust hand calipers as a gage. Stood on their ends (and with certain modifications), vernier calipers become height gages and depth gages. Protractors designed for layout work and for direct comparison of angular dimensions, can also be used as gages for checking work. At the other extreme, dial indicators, which are specifically designed as gages, are sometimes adapted to take overall direct measurements. Within the two extremes there are gages that are purely and simply indirect comparators. These are the fixed-size and limit gages.

For the purpose of discussion in this textbook, we have generally classified the instruments and gages used in the shop for dimensional measurement and control as: hand instruments; fixed-size or limit gages; instruments or gages utilizing mechanical, optical, electrical, or pneumatic amplifying systems (the indicating means of comparators); and measuring machines.

METHODS OF MEASUREMENT

The two basic methods of measurement are: direct comparison with a standard, and indirect comparison with a standard through the use of a calibrated system. "Standard" here refers to the practical, working level of standards—usually the two basic types consisting of end standards and line standards. Typical end standards are gage blocks, plug gages, and ring gages, each of which defines a single dimension. Line standards are the various types of instruments that have scales, and range from the simple rule to the laser beam. Line standards can be graduated in many ways, and each can define a multitude of lengths.

Indirect Comparison Measurement

Many other types of measurement require the use of an intermediate instrument called a *comparator*. For external length or diameter measurement, the comparator (sometimes called a *transfer* instrument) usually takes the form of a contact instrument in which a measuring plunger or stylus makes contact over the workpiece resting on a table or reference surface. Comparators depend on an external standard, and have a limited range of reading.

Direct Comparison Measurement

As a simple example of direct comparison measurement, you could use a steel rule or steel tape to measure the length of a cold-rolled bar of steel. Thus, to measure the bar, you compare its length with a line standard. The bar is so many units (inches, feet, centimeters, meters) long, because that many units on the standard equal the length of the bar. You determined this measurement by making a direct comparison with a working standard defining the unit. However, the standard that you use could undoubtedly trace its ancestry directly back through only three or four generations to the international standard of length, the specified wavelength from krypton-86.

Fig. 1-14   Common measuring instruments and setup tools used in the machine shop: (1) protractor, (2) OD caliper, (3) 6 in. rule, (4) 6 in. rule with shoulder stop, (5) depth micrometer, (6) combination square, (7) taper gages, (8) inside micrometer, (9) precision cylindrical square, (10) surface finish indicator and stylus, (11) telescoping gages, (12) divider, (13) precision straightedge, (14) dial caliper, (15) thickness gages, (16) inside indicator gage, (17) adjustable parallels, (18) vernier height gage, (19) radius gages, and (20) precision V-blocks.

THE MATHEMATICS OF MEASUREMENT

The machinist is primarily concerned with the precise measurement of lines, surfaces, solid forms and angles. Thus, a grasp of the practical principles of plane and solid geometry and right-angle trigonometry is necessary to put the measurement principles contained in this text into practice. The student should also understand Cartesian coordinates in three dimensions and be able to use algebra to manipulate equations and formulas. (Refer to NTMA's *Practical Mathematics for Metalworking Trainees*.)

LINEAR MEASUREMENT

Length, width, height, thickness, depth, circumference, and diameter, are measured in *linear units*, such as inches, feet, millimeters, centimeters, meters, etc. Linear measurements are the most common measurements made in the machine shop. They are made with many different measuring instruments (see Fig. 1-14). The measuring instrument used varies with the size of the dimension, the shape of the workpiece, and the degree of accuracy required. Direct-reading instruments used for linear measurement include the steel rule, micrometer, vernier caliper, vernier height gage, and the various depth gages. Indirect-reading instruments used for linear measurement include the caliper, divider, surface gage with dial test indicator, and telescoping gage. Related tools, such as straightedges, levels, surface gages, and steel squares, are used with linear measuring instruments to determine flatness, straightness, and squareness.

Measurements are usually made on round work using both direct- and indirect-reading instruments having contact points or surfaces, such as spring calipers, micrometers, and vernier calipers. You can make contact measurements in either of two ways:

(1) By first pre-setting the tool to the required dimension, using a steel rule, micrometer, or other instrument as a gage, and then comparing the set dimension with the actual size of the workpiece, or

(2) The reverse of the above; that is, to first set the contact points to the surfaces of the workpiece, and then—using a steel rule, vernier caliper, or micrometer—reading the size.

The first method is generally recommended where you are making repeated tests, such as in machining a piece to a given size, or when checking the same dimension on a number of identical parts. The second method is recommended for determining the actual size of the piece, or taking an accurate measure of variation from a specified tolerance (gaging).

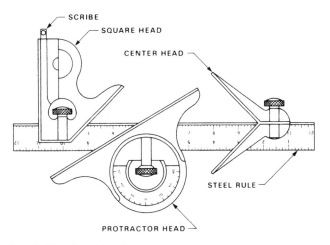

Fig. 1-15 Combination set.

ANGULAR MEASUREMENT

In machining precision parts, you will also be required to measure angles. Recall that an angle is the amount of opening between two straight lines converging at a point. The point of their intersection is called the *vertex*.

Angles are measured in degrees (deg or °), which are further subdivided into minutes (') and seconds (").

You can measure angles using squares, spirit levels, the combination set bevel protractor (see Fig. 1-15), the universal bevel protractor, sine bars and sine plates, precision angle gage blocks, index heads, or rotary tables.

MEASURING AREA AND VOLUME

In addition to measurements of length and angle, the machinist sometimes makes two related kinds of measurement: (1) area, and (2) volume. *Area* is the measurement of a plane surface of an object in two dimensions. *Volume* is the measurement of the space taken up or enclosed by anything—such as the surfaces of an object—in three dimensions.

INSTRUMENT SELECTION AND CORRECTION FACTORS

You have learned that there is inherent error in all measurements to some degree, some of which is due to instrument error. Therefore, you must evaluate the characteristics that describe an instrument or a comparator sensor before selecting it for a particular purpose. These characteristics include: accuracy, hysteresis, sensitivity and resolution, precision, amplification, range, parallax, discrimination, and calibration.

Accuracy

Although it sounds backward, the *accuracy* of an instrument is expressed by the amount of the instrument's error. For example, an instrument having an accuracy of 1% is said to have an error of ±1%.

The error of an instrument is actually the difference between the reading shown on the instrument and the true value of the variable being measured. Because the true value of the variable can never be known, the best that can be done is to estimate the amount of the error by various statistical means. This estimate is called the *uncertainty*. Error can be expressed in scale units, in percent of scale span, in percent of range, or in percent of indicated value. By agreement among instrument manufacturers, error in instruments having uniform scales is most commonly expressed as a percentage of the full scale length, regardless of where a measurement is made on the scale. The exception to this general rule is that a measurement should not be made either at the extreme top or the extreme bottom of the scale, because an instrument is almost sure to be less accurate in these areas than in the working range of the scale.

Hysteresis

If an instrument does not give the same reading from the top of the scale down to the point of measurement as it does from the bottom of the scale up to the point of measurement, the error is called *hysteresis*. For example, even though the contact points return to the same position, the indicator does not return to its initial position. Hysteresis results from the interaction of a variety of factors that cause loss of energy within the instrument, such as friction, binding of parts, fatigue of a spring, excessive play in gears, or other mechanical difficulties.

Sensitivity and Resolution

Instrument sensitivity is sometimes confused with instrument accuracy and discrimination, but the characteristics are quite different. The same factors that affect the amount of hysteresis displayed by an instrument affect its sensitivity. For mechanical indicating-type instruments that operate a moving pointer, *sensitivity* is the ratio of the instrument's response to the magnitude of the measured variable. In this case, sensitivity is measured by how far the contact points of the instrument must move before a change is indicated on the dial. In this case, sensitivity is directly related to the friction within the instrument. An instrument that has relatively small energy losses because of friction will generally be more sensitive than an instrument having relatively large friction losses. Other comparators, such as optical,

pneumatic, and electronic types, avoid some or all of the causes of low sensitivity.

For instruments having incremental display (digital readout), the term *resolution* is used, instead of sensitivity. Resolution relates to the smallest change in measured value to which the digital readout instrument will respond.

Precision

The repeatability of a measurement process is called its *precision*. This means how well a large number of identically-performed measurements agree with each other, and applies to a process or a *set* of measurements, not to a single measurement. Although many instruments have a high repeatability initially, they gradually lose calibration due to a tendency to *drift* from the correct value in the interval between calibrations. Such instruments require periodic checking and adjustment.

Amplification

Amplification is the ratio of the movement of an instrument's contact points to the movement of the measurement indicator on the scale. An instrument with too low an amplification tends to conceal essential variations. Choosing too high an amplification for the job can result in very irregular data that are equally misleading.

Range

The contact points of the instrument must move sufficiently to handle the maximum variation of the part dimension being checked. If the movement is adequate, the scale and indicating system must be able to measure sizes throughout the range. With few exceptions, wide-range instruments have low amplification, and high-amplification instruments have a narrow range.

Parallax

Instruments that require the user's eye to be in a specific alignment with the scale or indicator to obtain an accurate reading are said to have *parallax*, or an apparent difference in position. Instruments designed with the indicator as a thin vane perpendicular to the scale minimize or eliminate this characteristic, by forcing the eye to line up properly when reading the indicator.

Discrimination

Discrimination refers to the degree of fineness to which a scaled instrument divides the unit of measurement used for length. A micrometer, for example, subdivides 1 in. into 1,000 or, in some cases, 10,000 parts. Therefore, the micrometer is said to discriminate to 0.001 in. (0.01mm) thimble scale or 0.0001 in. (0.002mm) vernier scale. *No measuring instrument should be used beyond its capability for discrimination. Also, discrimination should not be interpreted as the ability to take an exact measurement to the discrimination unit of the instrument. A micrometer with a discrimination of 0.0001 in. is not reliable for measurements to 0.0001 in. It is generally good practice not to take measurements to the exact discrimination of an instrument, but to work to plus or minus one discrimination unit.*

Calibration

Before you use any measuring instrument, be sure that its calibration has been recently checked. In the list of instrument characteristics described above, note that sensitivity, repeatability, drift, and hysteresis can all affect the behavior of an instrument. Whenever an instrument is used by a number of people on a variety of parts, calibration becomes very critical.

PROPER USE OF HAND INSTRUMENTS

Hand/held measuring instruments have varying capabilities of discrimination ranging down to about 0.0001 in. or 0.002mm. The degree of accuracy required by the job indicates which particular instrument should be used. Linear measurements can only be as accurate as the capability of the instrument, its calibration, and the "feel" of the user.

For example, feel is of basic importance in obtaining accurate readings from a steel rule to compensate for parallax. In using a rule to measure from a shoulder or step, be sure to hold it firmly and squarely against the reference surface, as shown in Fig. 1-16.

Steel rules are sometimes used with calipers to take indirect measurements. For example, outside

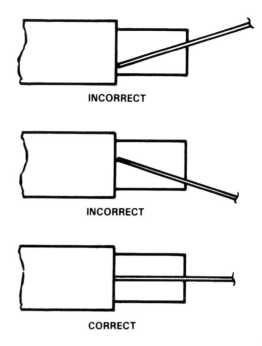

INCORRECT

INCORRECT

CORRECT

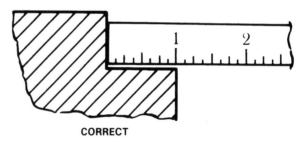

CORRECT

Fig. 1-16   Correct way to position a steel rule when measuring a shoulder.

diameter calipers are used to measure the diameter of a groove on a part being turned in a lathe. Again, feel is critical to accurate measurement. First, set the calipers so that they just contact the workpiece on both sides. Then, use the setting screw to make fine adjustments until both legs make firm (but not clamping-pressure) contact with the workpiece, and the legs are positioned squarely across the center of the workpiece to obtain the accurate reading. Finally, lay the calipers carefully against a steel rule and read the dimension.

Inside diameter calipers are used much like OD calipers, except that "feel" is obtained by moving the calipers up and down within the part

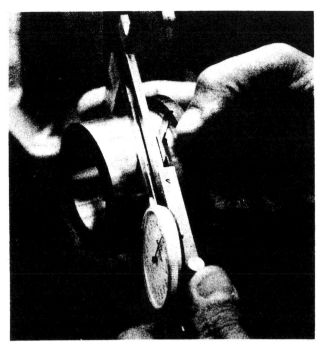

A – INCORRECT

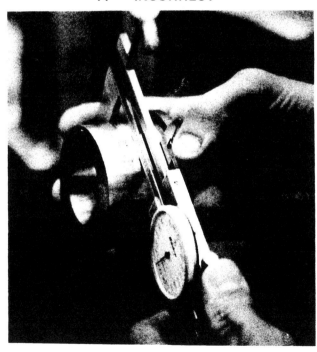

B – CORRECT

Fig. 1-17   *Measuring instruments of any type must be applied properly in order to provide accuracy. Here, the dial caliper must be applied squarely to the axis of the workpiece in order to accurately measure the diameter.*

until the legs just touch when the calipers are aligned with the horizontal axis.

In most cases today such measurements would be made directly with a vernier or dial-type caliper, as in Fig. 1-17. However, feel and proper use is still as important, even with the more sophisticated instruments.

CARE OF PRECISION INSTRUMENTS

As modern production methods demand increasing part accuracy, gages and measuring tools become more and more important in assuring product conformance to specifications. Not only do higher accuracy requirements demand instruments of greater complexity, but they also take more skillful use, meticulous care, and proper maintenance for a reasonable assurance of quality control.

Instruments expected to perform such delicate and important tasks as determining sizes and shapes within thousandths and sometimes millionths of an inch deserve the greatest care. Although all instruments are constructed from materials that provide the hardest contact surfaces for the greatest stability and accuracy, dirt remains the most frequent cause of excessive wear. Many instruments, to accomplish their purpose, make physical contact with the surfaces being checked. In nearly all of these contacts, friction occurs, such as when sliding a ring gage over a shaft, or a plug gage into a hole. A close look at the film normally present on the surface of both the gage and the part being checked will show a large content of abrasives. Thus, through use in the presence of abrasive dirt, the surfaces of the gage are continually wearing away and destroying the accuracy to which it was calibrated when new. Obviously, if the contact surfaces are kept clean, the life and performance of each instrument are greatly preserved.

Measuring tools and gages should always be stored where dirt and dust will not accumulate. Also, to avoid corrosion, temperature variations should not be excessive and relative humidity should never exceed 50%. If such an area is not available, all exposed surfaces of steel tools and gages should be covered with a corrosion-preventive coating of lubricating oil when not in use.

CHAPTER I REVIEW

1. If Noah's Ark was 50 cubits wide by 300 cubits long, what were its dimensions in feet if one cubit = 18 inches?

2. Read the following dimensions aloud:

   a) $^9/_{64}$ f) .50   k) 0.20mm   p) $^{13}/_{32}$
   b) .010   g) .500   l) 1.5m   q) $1^{23}/_{32}$
   c) .625   h) .5000   m) .9531   r) 1.2969
   d) $^7/_{32}$ i) .0001   n) 3.750   s) .875
   e) .5   j) .1   o) 2,175mm   t) .073

3. Write the following dimensions in numerical form:
   a) three thirty-seconds
   b) one hundred-eleven thousantdhs
   c) fifty thousandths
   d) one-and-a-half thousandths
   e) two "tenths"
   f) point oh-twenty-five millimeter
   g) two thousand millimeters
   h) oh-thirty-six
   i) one and a half tenths
   j) one hundred twenty-five thou

4. True or False? "Frequent inspections add quality to the finished product" — Discuss in class.

5. At a temperature of 68°F, a brass bar is exactly 10.0000 inches long. What is the length of the same bar when the temperature is 98°F?
   a) 10.0030″   b) 9.9970″   c) The same length as at 68°F
   Explain your answer.

6. Ten apprentices have measured the same piece using the same micrometer. Seven different micrometer readings were obtained among the ten trainees. What was the most likely source of error?

7. Describe the difference between measuring instruments and gages.

8. Describe the difference between direct-reading and indirect-reading measurement.

9. A passenger riding in the front seat of a car looks over at the speedometer and says to the driver, "You can speed up a little, the limit here is 55." The driver, irritated, says, "I *am* doing 55!" Which of the following words describes the passenger's reading of the speedometer?
   a) Hysteresis   b) Resolution   c) Amplification   d) Parallax

10. Describe some of the precautions that should be taken when storing or handling precision measuring instruments.

Chapter II

Measuring with Basic Graduated Instruments

Many hand-held measuring instruments and tools are used in the shop, because machinists must measure with a much greater degree of precision than is required in another line of work, such as carpentry. The most common direct-reading instruments used to make linear measurements on plane geometric shapes are the: steel rules, micrometers, vernier calipers, and depth gages. Various types of micrometers are designed to read inside, outside, and depth measurements to thousandths (0.001) of an inch. Vernier micrometers are graduated in ten-thousandths (0.0001) of an inch, and are read the same way as micrometer calipers.

The vernier caliper is another instrument that will discriminate to one-thousandth (0.001) of an inch. The vernier system of measurement is also used on other measuring instruments, such as height gages and bevel protractors.

STEEL RULES

The most common measuring instrument in the shop is the steel rule, which is made from tempered steel that is carefully ground and accurately graduated into inches and fractional inches. For example, the common inch rule usually has one side graduated into eighths and sixteenths, and the other into thirty-seconds and sixty-fourths, although various combinations of graduations in both the metric and English units of measure are available. The steel rule is satisfactory for deter-

mining *approximate* dimensions in rough machining work, layout work, checking to specifications, and many other shop applications. However, machinists with considerable skill and experience can attain a reasonably high degree of accuracy in measuring with a rule and calipers.

NOTE: The steel rule is *not a scale*. A scale *looks like* a steel rule, because its surface is graduated into regular divisions. However, the graduations on a scale differ from those on a steel rule in that they stand for units of measure that are either larger or smaller than those indicated. For example, a half-size scale is graduated so that 1 in. on the scale is equal to an actual measurement of 2 in. Therefore, a 12 in. scale is actually equal to 24 in. Thus, a scale gives *proportional measurements* instead of the actual measurements obtained with a rule. Scales are made from wood, plastic, or metal, and generally range from 6 to 24 in. in length. They are commonly used when working from scale drawings.

Shrink rules are a special type of scale designed for laying out wood and metal patterns, core boxes, etc. in the casting of metals. Their graduations permit shrink allowances to be read directly. Whereas inch shrink rules are designated in fractions-of-an-inch of shrink per foot, the metric shrink rules are graduated in percentage of shrink.

Steel rules are manufactured in three basic types of graduations in lengths ranging from 1 in.

to 14 ft.:

(1) Common inch fractions in halves ($\frac{1}{2}$), quarters ($\frac{1}{4}$), eighths ($\frac{1}{8}$), sixteenths ($\frac{1}{16}$), thirty-seconds ($\frac{1}{32}$), and sixty-fourths ($\frac{1}{64}$),

(2) Decimal inch fractions in divisions of one-tenth (0.1) and one-hundredth of an inch (0.01 in.), and

(3) Millimeters and half-millimeters (1.0 and 0.5mm).

Fig. 2-1 compares the fractional inch, decimal inch, and metric graduations in terms of inches and millimeters.

Figure 2-1: Steel Rule Graduations.

Unit	Equivalent Size	
	Inch	Millimeter
Fractional Inch: $\frac{1}{64}$ in.	0.0156	0.397
Decimal Inch: 0.01 in.	0.0100	0.254
Metric: 0.5mm	0.0197	0.500

Rigid Steel Rules

The 6 in. rigid steel rule (also called a *pocket rule* and a *machinist's rule*) is made from spring-tempered steel, and both sides are graduated into divisions of $\frac{1}{8}$, $\frac{1}{16}$, $\frac{1}{32}$, and $\frac{1}{64}$ in., as shown in Fig. 2-2.

Some 6 in. rules have graduations scribed on their ends, as shown in Fig. 2-3. This arrangement can be used to measure the depths and widths of grooves, countersinks, and recesses.

As you learned in the previous chapter, *discrimination* describes the extent to which a unit of length has been divided on a graduated measuring instrument. If the smallest graduation on a rule is 0.01 in., then that rule is said to discriminate to 0.01

Fig. 2-2 The 6 in. rigid steel rule. (Courtesy of The L. S. Starrett Company)

Fig. 2-3 A 6 in. rigid steel rule with graduations scribed on the ends. (Courtesy of Brown & Sharpe Manufacturing Company)

in. Likewise, if the smallest graduation on another rule is 1.0mm, then this rule discriminates to 1.0mm.

The discrimination of any steel rule is usually $\frac{1}{64}$ in. or, in the case of the decimal inch rule, 0.01 in. The metric rule generally discriminates down to 0.5mm. *No measuring tool should ever be used beyond its discrimination.* Therefore, a steel inch rule is not reliable for taking a measurement smaller than 0.01 or $\frac{1}{64}$ in. If a specific measurement falls between the graduations on the rule, you can only say that the measurement is *more or less* than the amount of the nearest mark; that is, you can only make approximate rather than precise measurements with the rule.

Thus, you can satisfactorily measure dimensions that have an allowable variation (tolerance) of $\frac{1}{64}$ in., *more or less*, with a steel rule, but only then under certain conditions. The surfaces or edges being measured must be clean and square, the light must be adequate, the scale must bear firmly against the work and align with the dimension being measured, and the scale itself must be in good condition. Of particular importance is the point on the rule from which the measurement is taken. This is called the *reference point*, and it must be carefully aligned with the corresponding point on the dimension being measured, taking care to eliminate any parallax.

It is always good practice to take more than one reading when using a steel rule. After determining the dimension once, apply the rule again to make sure you obtain the same result. This procedure increases the reliability of your measurement.

Flexible Rules

Another common 6 in. rule is the flexible rule shown in Fig. 2-4. It is narrower than the rigid steel rule ($\frac{1}{2}$ in. wide), and is made from thin ($\frac{1}{64}$ in.) tempered spring steel so that you can bend it a reasonable amount to take measurements in close quarters.

FRONT

BACK

Fig. 2-4   Flexible steel rule with English/metric conversion at centerline. (Courtesy of Brown & Sharpe Manufacturing Company)

Hook Rules

The hook rule (see Fig. 2-5) has one or two 90 deg arms or hooks projecting from the zero division at one end of the rule. The hooks may be either rigidly attached or adjustable. A hook helps to eliminate error in aligning the reference point to the workpiece so that you can read the accurate dimension from the rule.

Fig. 2-5   Hook rule. (Courtesy of Brown & Sharpe Manufacturing Company)

Hook rules make it possible to take accurate measurements in slots and against shallow shoulders, as shown in Fig. 2-6. They are also very useful for taking measurements of flanges, circular pieces, or through-holes; setting calipers and dividers; and taking measurements from reference points that the user could not see if an ordinary rule were aligned with the measuring edge.

Short Rule Set with Holder

The steel rule set with holder, shown in Fig. 2-7, is easy to use when measuring recesses. The set consists of a long tubular handle with a split chuck for holding any one of the graduated rules in the set. The chuck can be adjusted by a knurled nut at the end of the handle to hold a rule at various angles. The rules in the set generally range from $1/4$ in. to 1 in. in length.

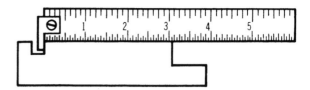

Fig. 2-6   One of many uses of the hook rule. (Courtesy of The L. S. Starrett Company)

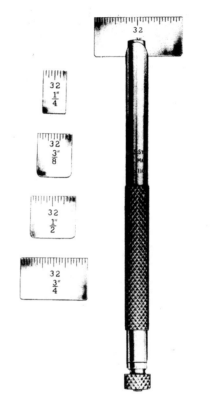

Fig. 2-7   Short rule set with holder. (Courtesy of The L. S. Starrett Company)

ACCESSORIES FOR GRADUATED RULES

By attaching different devices to a steel rule, you can increase its usefulness in measuring linear dimensions. Common accessories for the steel rule are: rule clamps, right angle clamps, key seat clamps, and rule holders.

Rule Clamps

A rule clamp (see Fig. 2-8) is used to clamp two steel rules together, end to end, for measuring lengths longer than can be measured with a single rule. Because the clamp bolts are independently

Fig. 2-8   Rule clamp used to lengthen a steel rule by joining it to another. (Courtesy of The L. S. Starrett Company)

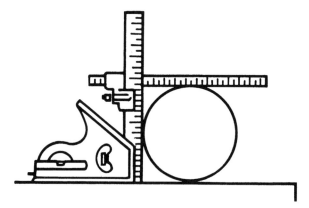

Fig. 2-10   Right angle rule clamp can be used to measure large diameters.

adjustable, the rule clamp will hold rules of the same or different widths.

Right Angle Clamps

A right angle rule clamp is used to fasten two rules together into a 90 deg angle (see Fig. 2-9). As shown in Fig. 2-10, such an arrangement is useful in measuring the diameter of large pieces.

Key Seat Clamps

Key seat clamps (Fig. 2-11A) are used to convert ordinary steel rules, combination square blades, and straightedges into *key seat rules* for laying out keyways and scribing parallel lines on round work. The thumb-screws allow the clamps to be attached or removed easily. As shown in Fig. 2-11B, unless the clamps are used, it is difficult to align the rule with the axis of the workpiece, resulting in inaccurate measurements.

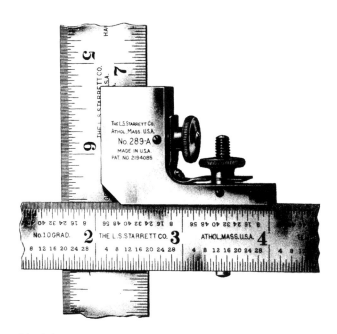

Fig. 2-9   Right angle rule clamp. (Courtesy of The L. S. Starrett Company)

A

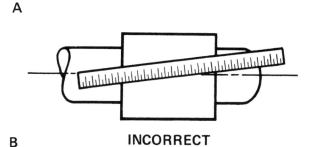

B   INCORRECT

Fig. 2-11   Key seat clamps align a rule with the axis of round work for accurate measurements. (Courtesy of The L. S. Starrett Company)

Rule Holders

A rule holder (see Fig. 2-12) is designed to hold rules perpendicular to a surface plate for use in transferring measurements with surface gages, etc. The knurled clamp nut locks the rule in the holder. This arrangement can also be used as a depth gage. In addition to rules, the holder can be used with combination square blades.

A

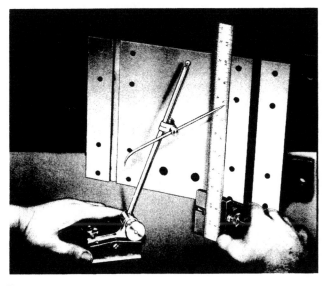

B

Fig. 2-12   A typical rule holder (A). Transferring measurements using a surface gage, a 12 in. rule, and a rule holder (B). (Courtesy of The L. S. Starrett Company)

MICROMETERS

As you learned earlier in this chapter, the smallest measurement you can make using the inch steel rule is 0.01 in. or $^1/_{64}$ in. Therefore, to make precise measurements on the order of thousandths and ten-thousandths of an inch, you must use a micrometer, often called a *"mike."* This instrument measures precise distances by recording the endwise travel of a screw during a whole turn, or any part of a turn of the screw.

Selecting the Right Micrometer

Micrometers are manufactured in many styles, but the major ones are: outside, inside, screw thread, and depth. They are also manufactured in a variety of frame sizes ranging from $^1/_2$ to about 48 in. However, the most commonly used is the outside micrometer in the 1 in. size, which measures from zero to 1.000 in. Because the thimble of a 1 in. micrometer travels a maximum of only 1 in., larger measurements require larger frames. For example, a 2 in. micrometer has a measuring range from 1 to 2 in., and a 6 in. micrometer has a measuring range from 5 to 6 in.

The micrometer is the most accurate of the adjustable direct-reading measuring instruments. It is used to read within one-thousandth (0.001) of an inch using the English system of measurement. If it is equipped with a vernier scale, it will read within one ten-thousandth (0.0001) of an inch in the English system. Metric micrometers will read within one-hundredth of a millimeter (0.01mm) or, when equipped with a vernier, to two-thousandths of a millimeter (0.002mm).

Outside Micrometer

The major parts of an outside inch micrometer graduated in thousandths of an inch are shown in Fig. 2-13. You should learn the names of these parts, because we can discuss the use of a micrometer only by using them. The *anvil face* is one of the two measuring faces between which the work is measured. The anvil is mounted in the frame opposite the spindle, as shown in Fig. 2-13. The *spindle face* is the other of the two measuring faces of a micrometer. A clockwise rotation of the thimble causes the spindle to move toward the

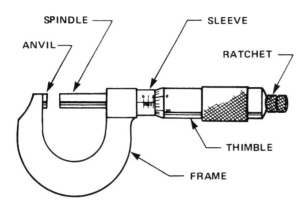

Fig. 2-13   *The major parts of an outside micrometer.*

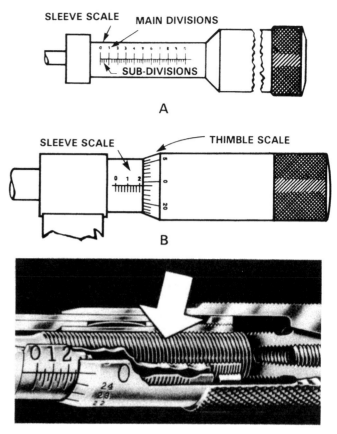

Fig. 2-15   *Main and subdivisions on micrometer sleeve scale (A) and thimble scale (B). Spindle screw (C). (Courtesy of The L. S. Starrett Company)*

anvil, whereas a counterclockwise rotation of the thimble causes the spindle to move away from the anvil. The *frame*, which holds the anvil in place, is held in the user's hand when measuring with the micrometer, as shown in Fig. 2-14.

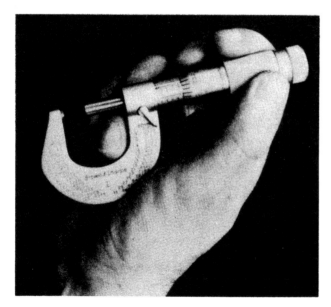

Fig. 2-14   *How to hold a micrometer correctly in the hand. Note positions of the fingers. (Courtesy of Brown & Sharpe Manufacturing Company)*

The *sleeve scale* of the micrometer is divided into ten main parts (see Fig. 2-15A), each part equaling one-hundred thousandths of an inch (0.100). Each main division on the sleeve is then sub-divided into four equal parts of twenty-five thousandths (0.025) of an inch, as shown in Fig. 2-15B.

The *thimble scale* has a beveled edge that is divided into 25 equal parts (see Fig. 2-15B), each part equaling one-thousandth of an inch (0.001). These graduations are marked, for convenience, at every five parts by 0, 5, 10, 15, and 20. One complete turn of the thimble will move the spindle twenty-five thousandths (0.025) of an inch.

The spindle screw (see Fig. 2-15C) allows a micrometer to measure. This screw has a pitch of 40 threads per inch, or $1/40$ in. Thus, a single revolution from one screw thread to the next moves the spindle $1/40$ in., or twenty-five thousandths (0.025) in. (1.000 in. divided by 40 equals 0.025 in.). Therefore, turning the thimble 40 complete revolutions moves the spindle exactly 1 in. A clockwise turn moves the spindle toward the anvil; a counterclockwise turn moves the spindle away from the anvil.

Some micrometers are equipped with a ratchet stop or with a friction thimble mechanism to control pressure on the work and thus helping to insure uniform and consistent accuracy. The ratchet stop (which looks like a small extension on the end of the thimble) is used to rotate the spindle until a predetermined amount of contact pressure is reached. At that point, the ratchet locks the spindle, preventing further turning. In this way, uniform readings are obtained even when different people use the same micrometer.

The friction thimble micrometer uses a mechanism built into the upper section of the thimble. The lower section of the thimble remains integral with the screw permitting "direct feel" of the measurement. The friction thimble type micrometer assures uniform contact pressure independent of the user's touch and permits one-hand operation of the micrometer.

Reading the Inch Micrometer — The sleeve and thimble scales of a micrometer caliper have been enlarged in Fig. 2-16. Note that the scale on the sleeve is divided into 40 equal parts per inch. Every fourth graduation is numbered 1, 2, 3, 4, etc., representing 0.100 in., 0.200 in., etc. If you turn the thimble so that its edge touches the first graduation past the zero on the sleeve scale, the spindle has opened 0.025 in. If you turn the thimble to the second graduation, the spindle has moved 0.025 in. plus 0.025 in., or 0.050 in.

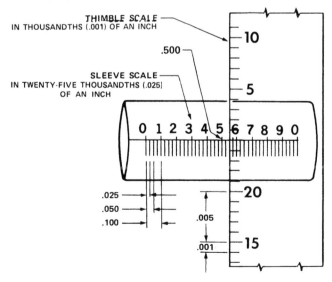

Fig. 2-16   Enlarged sleeve and thimble scales of an outside micrometer.

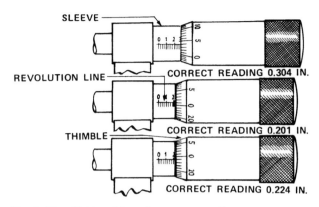

Fig. 2-17   Taking 1 in. micrometer readings.

You use the scale on the thimble to complete a reading when a measured dimension causes the edge of the thimble to stop between graduations. This scale is divided into 25 equal parts, each representing 1/25 of a complete revolution of the thimble, or 0.001 in. (0.025 in. divided by 25 equals 0.001 in.). As shown in Fig. 2-16, every fifth graduation on the thimble scale is marked 5, 10, 15 etc. The thimble scale permits you to take *very accurate* readings to thousandths of an inch and, because you can also estimate the distance between the graduations on the thimble scale, *fairly accurate* readings to one-half a thousandths (.0005) of an inch are possible.

The closeup views in Fig. 2-17 will help you learn how to take a complete micrometer reading in thousandths of an inch. Be sure to count the units on the thimble scale, and add them to the reading on the sleeve scale. The correct readings are given under each view in the figure so that you can check yourself.

Reading the Vernier Micrometer — When you are working to exceptionally precise dimensions, you should use a micrometer that discriminates to one ten-thousandth of an inch (0.0001) to make measurements. This degree of accuracy is obtained by a micrometer equipped with a vernier scale. A vernier scale (see Fig. 2-18) permits you to take precise fine readings between the lines on the thimble, rather than simply estimating them. Because, as shown in Fig. 2-18, the ten spaces on the vernier are equal to the nine spaces on the thimble, each space on the vernier scale equals 9/10 of one space on the thimble scale; the difference between the sizes of the graduations on each scale is 0.0001 in.

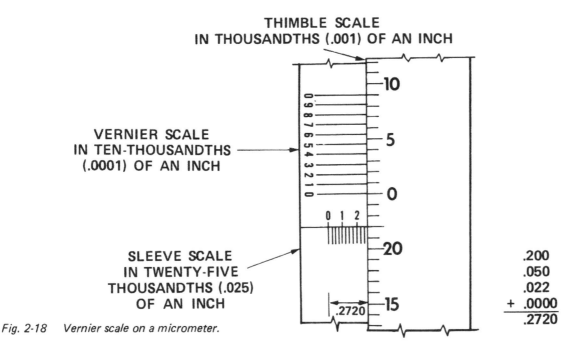

Fig. 2-18   Vernier scale on a micrometer.

Therefore, when a line on the thimble scale does not coincide with a line on the horizontal sleeve scale (as they do in Figs. 2-17 and 2-18), find the vernier graduation that coincides with a graduation on the thimble scale, and add that many ten-thousandths of an inch to the usual reading. In Fig. 2-18, you would add 0.0000 to the reading, as shown by the additional column.

However, in Fig. 2-19, only the second graduation on the vernier scale coincides with a graduation on the thimble scale. This means that the 0.011 mark on the thimble scale has advanced an additional 0.0002 in. beyond the horizontal sleeve scale. Adding this amount to the other readings gives 0.3362 in., as shown by the addition column.

Reading the Metric Micrometer — When you work with metric dimensions, you must use a metric micrometer caliper to make measurements. You read a metric micrometer (see Fig. 2-20A.) exactly the same as you do the inch micrometer. Both have a sleeve scale and a thimble scale and sometimes a vernier scale. The only difference is in the units of measure represented by the scale graduations.

The pitch of the spindle screw on a metric micrometer graduated in hundredths of a millimeter (0.01mm) is one-half millimeter, or 0.5mm. Therefore, one complete revolution of the thimble (clockwise or counterclockwise) moves the spindle face 0.5mm either toward or away from the anvil face. Thus, each thimble graduation equals $^{1}/_{50}$ of 0.5mm., or 0.01mm. Two revolutions of the thimble moves the spindle a full 1mm.

The sleeve scale on a metric micrometer (sometimes called the *index line* or the *reading line*) is graduated in millimeters above the line, and half-

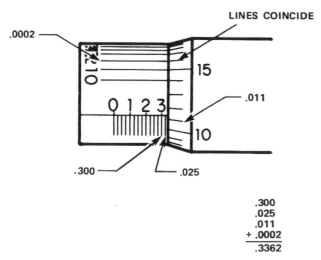

Fig. 2-19   Reading a vernier micrometer.

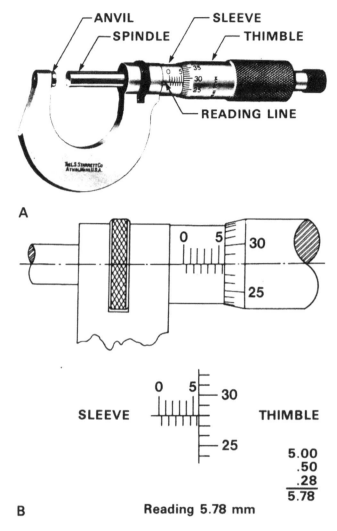

A

SLEEVE   THIMBLE

5.00
.50
.28
5.78

B   Reading 5.78 mm

Fig. 2-20   A metric micrometer.

stock to be measured in one hand. Hold the micrometer in the other hand so that the thimble rests between your thumb and the forefinger, as shown in Fig. 2-21. Your third finger is then in a position to hold the frame against the palm of your hand. This gives the frame support and makes it easy for you to guide the work over the anvil. Your thumb and forefinger can then turn the thimble either directly or through the friction thimble, and bring the spindle over against the surface being measured.

Turn the spindle screw down to contact the work either by "feel," or with the friction thimble. Your "feel" should produce the same contact pressure—and therefore the same reading—as that produced when you use the friction thimble providing the friction thimble was used when setting the micrometer with a round standard. You can develop your "feel" by measuring a certain dimension both with and without the aid of the friction thimble. When you have the correct "feel," you will get the same readings with both methods.

Your "feel" must be very light in measuring round stock because only a narrow line of contact runs between the spindle face and the stock, and the anvil face and the stock. Therefore, the contact area is exceptionally small, causing a proportionally high contact pressure per unit of area. This tends to give a reading smaller than the true reading if gage blocks were used for setting the micrometer using the friction thimble. This problem is overcome by using a lighter "feel."

millimeters below the line, as shown in Fig. 2-20B. Every fifth millimeter above the line is marked with a number: 5, 10, 15, 20, and 25. The thimble scale is divided into 50 equal parts. Every fifth division is numbered from 0 to 50 in increments of 5.

To read a measurement on a metric micrometer, first find the graduation line on the sleeve that coincides with the graduation line on the thimble. Then add the number of whole and half-millimeters visible on the sleeve scale to the number of hundredths of a millimeter shown on the thimble scale. For example, in Fig. 2-20B, adding 5mm to 0.50mm plus 0.28 gives a total reading of 5.78mm.

Measuring Round Stock — When measuring the diameter of a small piece of round stock, hold the

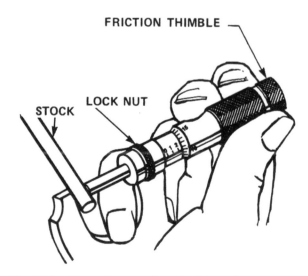

Fig. 2-21   Measuring round stock with a micrometer.

When measuring a ball from a ball bearing, contact is made at only two tiny points so that, again, the contact area is very small, resulting in a tremendous pressure per unit of area. This situation demands only the lightest possible contact pressure to give a true reading.

Hold the micrometer in your hand lightly, and for only as long as is necessary to make the measurement. However, wrapping your hand around the micrometer, or holding it for too long a time, will cause the metal to expand, which will introduce error into the measurement. If the object is small, read the setting on the thimble scale without removing the micrometer from the object.

Measuring a Flat Surface — When measuring a flat surface with a micrometer, such as the thickness of a piece of stock, the entire area of both the anvil and the spindle faces is in contact with the surface being measured. This causes a proportionally low contact pressure per unit of area. Therefore, your "feel" should be slightly heavier than when measuring round stock.

On large flat work, the work must be stationary, and positioned to permit access for the micrometer. The proper way to hold a micrometer when checking a part too large to be held in one hand is shown in Fig. 2-22. Hold the frame with one hand to position it and to locate it firmly against the measured surface. Use the other hand to operate the thimble, either directly or through the friction thimble. You should measure a large flat surface in several

places to determine the amount of any variation. It is good practice to lock the spindle in place with the locknut before removing the micrometer from the part being measured. This way, the measurement you read on the thimble scale after removing the micrometer will be as accurate as possible.

To retain a particular setting in cases where several pieces are to be measured, lock the spindle in place with the locknut. When "gaged" by a micrometer whose spindle is locked to a particular setting, a piece can quickly be identified as oversize, correct size, or undersize.

Inside Micrometers

The inside micrometer is designed to measure internal dimensions, such as the inside diameters of tubing and holes, the bore of cylinders, or the width of a recess. The measurements obtained are just as precise as those obtained with an outside micrometer. However, the nomenclature of inside micrometers differs slightly from that of other micrometers (see Fig. 2-23). Moreover, the range of an inside micrometer is usually only 0.500 in.

The *body* of the inside micrometer (often called the *head*) is composed of the units that are called the barrel and the thimble on an outside micrometer.

Fully closed, most inside micrometers are 1.5 in. long, which prohibits measuring dimensions

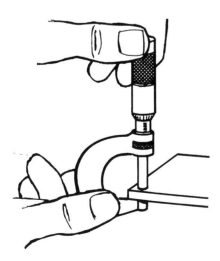

Fig. 2-22 Measuring flat stock with a micrometer.

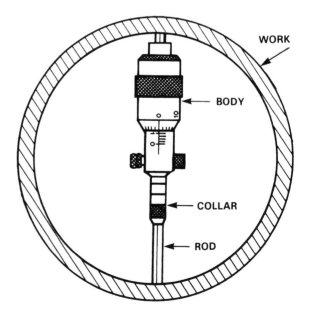

Fig. 2-23 Inside micrometer.

smaller than 1.5 in. However, when extension rods of various lengths are added, you can measure dimensions up to 100 in. and more. The maximum measurement possible is governed by the length of the longest extension rod available. On some inside micrometers, you can mount extension rods on both ends of the body, thereby further increasing the maximum measurement that can be obtained.

Measuring Hole Diameters — You read inside micrometers in the same way that you read outside micrometers, except that you must add the lengths of the body and any extension rods to the measurement. For example, using a 3 in. extension rod and an inside micrometer with a body length of 1.5 in., you obtain a reading of 0.358. What is the diameter of the hole?

3.000	Length of extension
1.500	Length of body
0.358	Reading obtained
4.858	Actual measurement

To measure holes ranging from 2 in. to several feet in diameter, select an inside micrometer having extension rods whose range includes the required dimension. For example, the extension rod marked "6-7," when inserted into the head of the micrometer, will measure inside diameters from 6 to 7 in. The shoulder on the rod must seat properly to ensure a correct reading. For large measurements, use both hands to position the micrometer for checking a diameter. Hold one end in place with one hand as you "feel" for the maximum possible setting by moving the other end from left to right, and simultaneously in and out of the hole with the other hand. When no more left-to-right movement is possible, and you notice a slight drag on the in-and-out swing, take the reading.

Remember not to handle an inside micrometer any longer than you have to, because your body heat can cause the metal to expand and produce significant errors.

You can use a jaw-type inside micrometer (such as the one shown in Fig. 2-24) to measure the diameter of small holes ranging from 0.2 to 1 in. in diameter. Note that the numbers on both the thimble and the barrel are reversed, increasing in the opposite direction from those on an outside micrometer. Thus, as you turn the thimble clockwise on this micrometer, the measuring surfaces

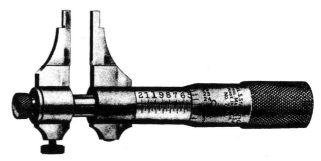

Fig. 2-24   Jaw-type inside micrometer. (Courtesy of The L. S. Starrett Company)

move farther apart as the reading increases. (On an outside micrometer, as you turn the thimble clockwise, the measuring surfaces move closer together and the reading decreases.) Small hole micrometers are discussed in Chapter VI.

Screw Thread Micrometers

Screw thread micrometers (see Fig. 2-25A) are used to measure the pitch diameter of screw threads to thousandths accuracy. This type of micrometer is graduated and read the same way as

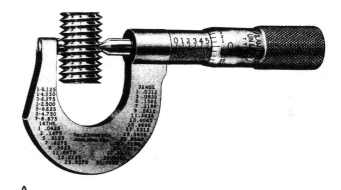

A

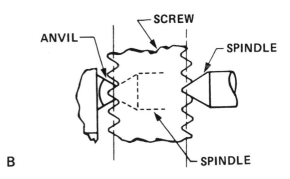

B

Fig. 2-25   Screw thread micrometer. (Courtesy of The L. S. Starrett Company)

outside micrometers. However, a double-V anvil and pointed spindle are ground to fit the shape of a screw thread, as shown in Fig. 2-25B.

Thread micrometers come in the same size ranges as ordinary micrometers: 0 to 1 in., 1 to 2 in., 0 to 25mm, 25 to 50mm, etc. In addition, they are available in various pitch ranges. To be acceptable, the number of threads per inch must be within the pitch range of the thread micrometer. A thread micrometer is probably the most accurate method of measuring pitch diameter. (NOTE: For more on other types of micrometers, see Chapter VI.)

Care of Micrometers

Micrometers are precision measuring tools, and must be handled with care to maintain their accuracy. One of the greatest abuses of an outside micrometer is to overtighten the spindle (turn the spindle too hard against the work or the anvil). Use only enough pressure to bring the anvil and the spindle against the surface of the work. A light pressure applied with the thumb and forefinger is adequate. Never tighten the micrometer enough to support its own weight.

The ratchet incorporated into many micrometers is actually a friction mechanism that is designed to slip if too much pressure is applied to the thimble. A knurled ring, located in the frame near the spindle on some micrometers, is designed to act as a spindle lock. When desirable turn the spindle lock after positioning the spindle; this will allow you to handle the micrometer without disturbing the setting.

Periodically the micrometer should be checked for calibration and adjusted, if required, and the anvil and spindle faces checked for parallelism. When you are not using the micrometer, place it gently on a smooth clean surface in a case or box. Be careful not to bump or drop it. Anvil faces must be protected from damage, and must not be cleaned with emery cloth or other abrasive. Coat the surface of the micrometer with a light film of clean oil. Never use dirty oil, or permit dirt particles to touch or accumulate on the micrometer—KEEP IT CLEAN.

VERNIER CALIPERS

When you must measure dimensions of varying lengths to tolerances in thousandths of an inch, the more versatile vernier caliper will allow greater measuring range than the micrometer, but will not give as precise a measurement. Because each size of micrometer has only a limited expansion capacity, you might have to use several frame sizes to make your measurements. The capacity of the vernier caliper, on the other hand, is limited only by the length of its scale, which can range from 2 in. (in the pocket type) to 4 ft. In addition, you can use the vernier caliper to make either external or internal measurements, as shown in Fig. 2-26. External measurements are taken by closing the *jaws* over the piece to be measured. Internal measurements (such as the diameter of a hole) are taken by opening up the *nibs* between the inside surfaces to be measured (see Fig. 2-26).

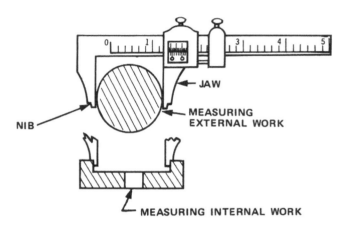

Fig. 2-26   *Vernier caliper.*

Thus, the vernier caliper is one of the most versatile—but not the most precise—precision measuring instruments available to the machinist. Most toolmakers and machinists prefer to purchase at least one good vernier caliper (along with a few micrometers) for their personal use on the job. Vernier calipers are available in many styles, and in inch graduations, metric graduations, or graduated in both inches and in millimeters. (NOTE: For more on precision calipers, see Chapter VI.)

Principles of the Vernier Scale

You learned a little about the vernier scale earlier in this chapter under "Vernier Micrometers." However, the vernier principle is so important to you in precision work that you should really understand it. As you know, sometimes the graduation on the thimble of the micrometer does not fall directly on an index line of the sleeve. Therefore, to make possible precision measurements smaller than thousandths, an ingenious device was introduced in the 1600s in the form of an additional scale. This scale, called a *vernier*, was named after its inventor, Pierre Vernier. The vernier makes possible accurate readings to one ten thousandths of an inch (0.0001).

Suppose that a decimal-inch rule has graduations every tenth of an inch, but it is necessary to read accurately to hundredths. A separate, freely-sliding vernier scale (see Fig. 2-27) is added to the rule, which has ten graduations on it that span the same distance as the nine graduations on the rule. Thus, each space on the vernier is 0.1 of 0.9 in., or 0.09 in. How much smaller is the space on the vernier than the space on the rule? The space on the rule is 0.10 in., and the vernier space is 0.09 in. Therefore, each vernier space is smaller by the difference between these two numbers, or 0.01 in.

DECIMAL-INCH RULE (ENLARGED)

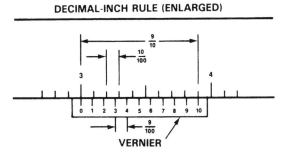

Fig. 2-27   Principle of the vernier scale.

As an example of the use of the vernier scale, suppose that you are measuring the steel bar shown in Fig. 2-28. The end of the bar almost reaches the 3 in. mark on the rule, and you estimate that it is about halfway between 2.9 in. and 3.0 in. The vernier graduations help you to decide whether

DECIMAL-INCH RULE (ENLARGED)

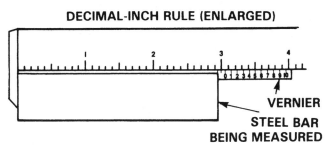

VERNIER
STEEL BAR
BEING MEASURED

Fig. 2-28   Measuring with a vernier.

the exact measurement is 2.94 in., 2.95 in., or 2.96 in.

The zero on the vernier scale is spaced the distance of exactly one rule graduation (in this case, 0.1 in.) from the left-hand end of the vernier. Therefore, the zero is at a position between rule graduations that is comparable to the position of the end of the bar. In other words, the zero on the vernier is about halfway between two adjacent graduations on the rule, just as the end of the bar is about halfway between two adjacent graduations on the rule. The 1 on the vernier scale is a little closer to alignment with an adjacent rule graduation; in fact it is 0.01 in. closer to alignment than the zero. This is because each space on the vernier is 0.01 in. shorter than each space on the rule.

Each successive graduation on the vernier scale is 0.01 in. closer to alignment than the preceding mark, until finally alignment is achieved at the 5 graduation. This means that the zero on the vernier must be 0.05 in. from the nearest rule graduation, because we passed five increments—each 0.01 in. in size—before we found a graduation in alignment.

Thus, you conclude that the end of the bar is 0.05 in. from the 2.9 graduation on the rule, because its position between graduations is exactly comparable to that of the zero on the vernier scale. Therefore, the value of the measurement is 2.95 in.

This example could be followed through for any distance between graduations. Suppose the zero graduation fell 0.7 of the distance between rule graduations. It would take seven vernier graduations (a loss of 0.01 in. each time) to bring the marks into alignment at 7 on the vernier.

The vernier principle is used to obtain fine angular measurements as well as linear measurements, as you will learn shortly. It always operates the same. The vernier has one more graduation than the number of graduations on an equal span of the conventional scale of the measuring instrument. For example, the vernier caliper has 25 graduations on the vernier for 24 on the caliper scale. The caliper is marked off to read to fortieths (0.025) of an inch, and the vernier extends the accuracy to a thousandth of an inch.

The vernier caliper is quite similar to the slide caliper rule, except that it has a vernier scale engraved on a small plate attached to the bar.

To make measurements with the vernier

caliper, you move the sliding jaw until you obtain the right "feel" on the work. An adjusting screw allows you to make fine adjustments on the jaws. To do this, first set the jaws to the approximate dimension, and lock the nut carrier. Then, by turning the adjusting nut, you can move the sliding jaw assembly very slowly in either direction. When you have the correct "feel" on the work, lock the sliding jaw in position for reading the vernier, or to hold the setting for subsequent measurements.

Reading the Inch Vernier Caliper – Figure 2-29 shows a 1 in. segment of the bar of a vernier caliper that is graduated into 40 parts, so that each graduation equals one-fortieth of an inch, or 0.025 in. Every fourth graduation is numbered; each number indicates tenths of an inch, or 0.1 in. (0.025 multiplied by 4 equals 0.100).

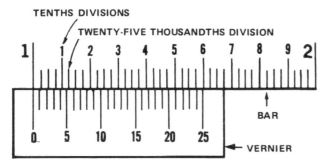

Fig. 2-29   Inch scale on a vernier caliper.

The vernier scale, which slides along the bar, is graduated into 25 divisions that are equal to the 24 divisions on the bar. Therefore, each division of the vernier scale is 0.001 in. smaller than each division on the bar. This type of vernier caliper is called an *inch vernier caliper.*

To read the inch vernier caliper shown in Fig. 2-30A, first write down in a column the number of inches (1.000), the number of tenths of an inch (0.400), and the number of thousandths of an inch that the zero mark on the vernier scale is past the zero mark on the bar (0.025). Then find the highest number on the vernier scale where a line on the vernier coincides with one on the bar. In this case, it is 0.011, so write 0.011 in the column, as shown next to Fig. 2-30A.

The total reading on this caliper is 1.436 in., obtained by adding the four separate readings in the column. With a little practice, you will be able

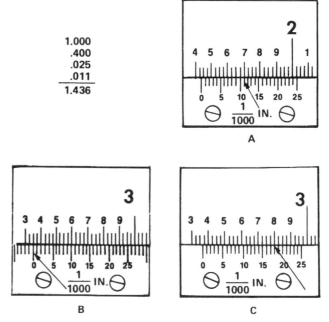

Fig. 2-30   Reading an inch vernier caliper.

to make these calculations mentally instead of writing them down.

Read the settings of the two vernier calipers shown in Figs. 2-30B and C, following the procedure described above. The total readings you should get are 2.350 in. on Fig. 2-30B, and 2.368 in. on Fig. 2-30C.

Reading the Metric Vernier Caliper – As with inch and metric micrometers, you read the metric vernier caliper exactly as you do the inch vernier caliper. The only difference is in the metric units of measure. On a metric vernier caliper that discriminates to 0.02mm, the bar scale is graduated into whole millimeters, usually with every tenth one numbered 10, 20, 30, etc. (see Fig. 2-31). Each of the divisions between the whole millimeters equals 0.50mm.

The vernier scale on the sliding jaw is divided into 25 equal spaces, with every fifth space numbered 0.10, 0.20, 0.30mm, etc. The five smaller divisions between the numbered lines each equal two-hundredths (0.02) of a millimeter.

To read a metric vernier caliper, first note the number of whole and half millimeters on the bar scale to the left of the zero on the vernier scale. Then add the number of 0.02mm from the vernier scale, indicated by the graduation on the vernier

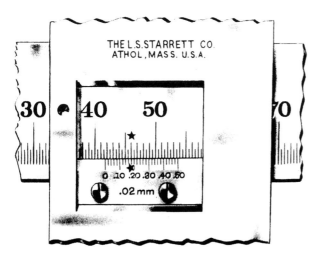

Fig. 2-31   Reading a metric vernier caliper. (Courtesy of The L. S. Starrett Company)

scale that coincides with a graduation on the bar scale.

For example, Fig. 2-31 shows that a graduation on the vernier scale coincides with a graduation on the bar scale at the 0.18mm graduation of the vernier scale. Thus, 0.18 should be added to the bar scale reading of 41.5mm, giving a total reading of 41.68mm.

Reading the Inch/Metric Vernier Caliper. Some vernier calipers are graduated in both inch and metric units of measure, as shown in Fig. 2-32. The metric scale appears on the top of the bar, and the inch scale on the bottom of the bar. The vernier scale is graduated into 50 parts. When taking inside measurements over the nibs with the inch/metric

caliper, you must add certain amounts to compensate for the thickness of the nibs. Caliper manufacturers provide this information with the caliper for their particular instrument.

Reading vernier scales accurately requires great care and a keen eye, but above all, *practice*. You may find that a magnifying glass will help you read vernier scales more quickly and accurately. A small, pocket-type magnifying glass with a folding cover is a very handy toolbox item for both apprentices and experienced journeymen.

Gear Tooth Vernier Calipers

The gear tooth vernier caliper (see Fig. 2-33) is used to measure both the thickness of a gear tooth on the pitch circle and the distance from the top of the tooth to the pitch chord, at the same time. The vernier scale on this instrument is read in the same way as other verniers.

To use the gear tooth vernier, first calculate the chordal addendum (a_c) and the chordal thickness (t_c) of the gear tooth using the gear formulas available in the standard reference handbooks. Suppose that a_c turned out to be 0.128 in. and t_c was 0.1962 in. Now set the vertical scale of the gear tooth vernier caliper to 0.128 in. Adjust the caliper so that the jaws touch each side of the tooth, as shown in Fig. 2-33. If the reading on the horizontal scale is 0.1962 in., the tooth has correct dimensions; if the dimension is greater, the tooth groove is too shallow; if the reading is less, the tooth groove is too deep.

Sometimes the outside diameter of a gear or the number of teeth cannot be determined from

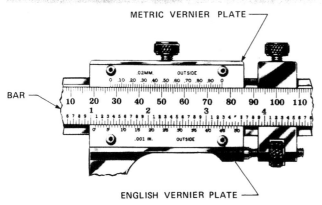

Fig. 2-32   Vernier caliper graduated in both inch and metric units. (Courtesy of The L. S. Starrett Company)

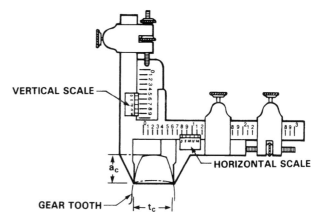

Fig. 2-33   Measuring a gear tooth with a vernier caliper.

available information. However, if you can obtain a gear dimension and a tooth dimension, you can key these dimensions into one or more of the gear formulas, and calculate the unknown dimensions.

Care of the Vernier Caliper

The inside faces of the caliper jaws and the outside of the nibs must be treated with great care. If they become worn, or the jaws become bent, the caliper will no longer give accurate readings.

The accuracy of vernier calipers should be checked periodically by measuring an object of known dimension. Vernier calipers can be adjusted when they are not accurate, but be sure to follow the manufacturer's recommendations for this adjustment. Keep vernier calipers lightly oiled to prevent corrosion, and keep them stored in a case or box away from heavy tools.

DEPTH GAGES

A depth gage is an instrument commonly used to measure the depth of holes, slots, counterbores, recesses, and the distance from a surface to a recessed part. Depth gages are especially useful to tool and diemakers for measuring depths on work where a gage with a permanent or fixed blade cannot be used. They are useful for measuring the depth of holes; recesses in dies, or the distance from a plane surface to a projection. Depth gages are available in various shapes and sizes with common English and metric rule, micrometer, or vernier graduations.

Rule Depth Gage

The rule depth gage (see Fig. 2-34A) consists of a graduated rule with a sliding head attached that is designed to bridge a hole or slot, and to hold the rule perpendicular to the surface on which the measurement is taken. It has a measuring range of 0 to 5 in. or 0 to 125mm.

The sliding head has a clamping screw that will fix the head at any dimension within the range of the rule. The horizontal flat base of the sliding head is set perpendicular to the axis of the rule, and ranges in width from 2 to $2^{5}/_{8}$ in.

Using the Rule Depth Gage

To measure the depth of a hole or slot with reasonable accuracy, you can use a rule depth gage, as shown in Fig. 2-34B. Hold the flat base against the surface from which the depth is to be measured, and extend the rule into the hole or slot. Tighten the setscrew to maintain the setting, and then withdraw the gage from the work and read the depth on the rule.

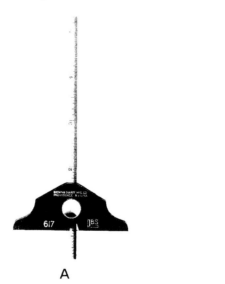

A

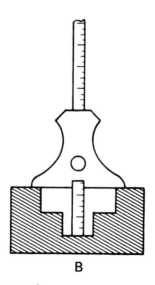

B

Fig. 2-34   Rule depth gage. (Courtesy of Brown & Sharpe Manufacturing Company)

Vernier Depth Gage

The vernier depth gage (see Fig. 2-35A) is similar in appearance to the rule depth gage, but is a precision measuring instrument. A vernier plate attached to the sliding head allows the depths of holes, slots, and recesses to be determined in thousandths (0.001) of an inch. The graduated blade has a measuring range of 0 to 6 in. or 0 to 12 in. The blade may be locked in place at any point with the fine adjustment mechanism, and read from the vernier on the head.

Using the Vernier Depth Gage

To measure the depth of a hole or slot with precision, place the flat base of a vernier depth gage over the slot as shown in Fig. 2-35B. In the drawing, notice the clamping screws labeled X and Y, and the horizontal adjusting screw nut labeled Z. First, loosen X and Y, and slide the rule down into the slot being measured until it is almost in contact. Then tighten X to make Z operative. Using Z, adjust the scale to the proper "feel," and lock the setting with Y. Proper "feel" means the adjustment at which you first notice contact between the end of the scale and the bottom of the slot. Finally, read the vernier scale.

To set the vernier depth gage to a particular setting, first loosen both X and Y, and slide the rule through the gage to the approximate setting. Then, tighten X, turn Z until the desired setting is made, and then tighten Y to hold the setting.

Micrometer Depth Gage

The micrometer depth gage is another very accurate instrument used for vertical measurements. It is also an essential tool for jig and fixture-making. The gage allows the depths of holes, slots, etc., to be measured to thousandths (0.001) of an inch.

The micrometer depth gage consists of a flat base attached to the thimble of a micrometer head. It has a measuring range from 0 to 6 in. or 0 to 150mm, depending on the length of extension rod

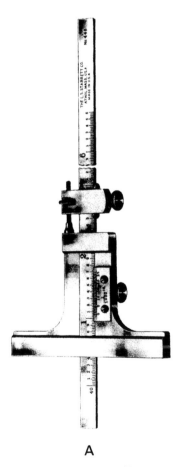

A

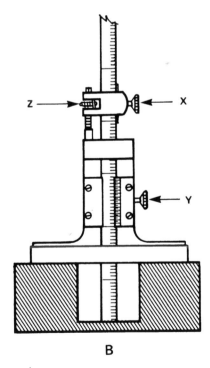

B

Fig. 2-35   Vernier depth gage. (Courtesy of The L. S. Starrett Company)

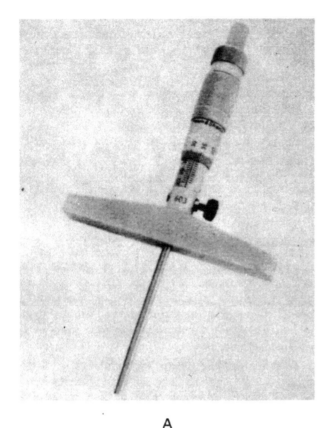

A

used (see Fig. 2-36A). The micrometer screw (the threads on which the thimble rotates) itself has a range of either 0.5 or 1 in. Some micrometer depth gages are provided with a ratchet stop. The flat base ranges in width from 2 to 6 in.

Using the Micrometer Depth Gage

To measure the depth of a hole or slot with more accuracy than is possible with a rule depth gage or with a vernier depth gage, place the flat base of a micrometer depth gage over the slot, as shown in Fig. 2-36B, and adjust the thimble until contact by the spindle causes the ratchet stop to slip. Remove the micrometer from the work, and take the reading. Remember, if extension rods are used, the total depth reading will be the sum of the length of the rods *plus* the reading on the micrometer.

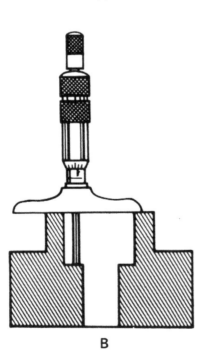

B

Fig. 2-36   Micrometer depth gage. (Courtesy of Brown & Sharpe Manufacturing Company)

CHAPTER II REVIEW

1. Explain the difference between a rule and a scale.

2. Why is it important to use a light touch when measuring round or spherical parts with an outside micrometer?

3. If an ordinary micrometer can be read to the nearest ten-thousandth of an inch, why is a vernier micrometer more desirable?

4. Describe two different ways of using the spindle lock on a micrometer.

5. Match the item to be measured with the appropriate measuring instrument:

    A) Length of a bar (about 5″ long) to ± .002″   a) Steel rule (in ¹/₆₄ th's)

    B) Diameter of a hole (about 2″∅) to ± .001″   b) Outside micrometer

    C) Length of a bar (about 5″ long) to ± .020″   c) Inside micrometer

    D) Thickness of a flat shim to ± .0005″   d) Vernier caliper

    E) Distance to bottom of a blind hole   e) Micrometer depth gage

6. Practice and be able to demonstrate to your instructor or supervisor the correct and accurate use of rules, micrometers and vernier instruments.

Chapter III

Angle Measuring Instruments

The instruments used to measure the magnitude of angles include: the square, the protractor, spirit levels, sine bars and sine plates, angle gages, precision angle gage blocks, index heads, and rotary tables.

SQUARES

A square is a measuring instrument consisting of two rules or two straightedges set at right angles (90 deg) to each other. They are used by machinists to check the trueness of right angles, as a guide when drawing lines on materials before cutting, and for locating holes. Many kinds of squares are used by machinists and toolmakers, depending on the accuracy required by the job. Because most squares have a scale marked on their edges, they are also used for making linear measurements.

Machinist's Squares

There are several variations of the machinist's square in common use, including the try square, bevel edge square, double square, diemaker's square, adjustable, and sliding T-bevel. These types of squares are sometimes called "hand squares" and are suitable for work with tolerances in thousandths of an inch. For closer work, a more accurate instrument should be used. (See Chapter V for more on squareness.)

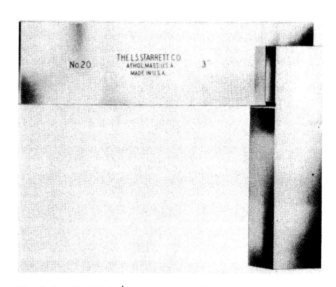

Fig. 3-1 Machinist's try square. (Courtesy of The L. S. Starrett Company)

Machinist's Try Square — The machinist's try square (see Fig. 3-1), which is sometimes called the *precision steel solid beam* or *hardened steel square*, is the most common type of machinist's square. It is used to lay out or check right angles and perpendiculars. It is also used to check right angles and in setting up work on shapers, milling machines, and drilling machines. Figure 3-2 shows how to use squares to test adjacent faces of a piece of work for squareness. The gap is either judged visually, or measured with a thickness gage.

The machinist's try square consists of two

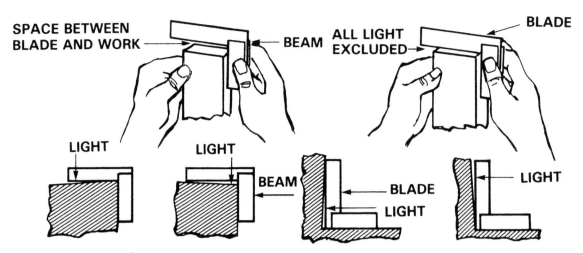

Fig. 3-2   *Using the machinist's square to test workpiece for squareness.*

parts—a thin steel blade and a thick beam—set at right angles to each other. In manufacturing this square, the steel beam and blade are first hardened, the edges of both the beam and the blade are carefully ground, and then they are lapped to exact trueness. This square has no scales and is, there-fore, not used for linear measurements. The length of the blade ranges from $1\frac{1}{2}$ to 36 in. with proportionally shorter beams. This precision tool will remain accurate only if you take special care of it. Do not allow it to contact other tools that could dent or nick its lapped edges or distort its 90 deg setting. Clean and polish it frequently to keep it from rusting, and store it in a safe place when you are not using it.

Thin Steel Try Square — This try square is a single piece of steel graduated on both sides of its blade and beam in inch fractions or millimeters (see Fig. 3-3). It looks like a carpenter's square, but smaller. The blade is only 6 in. long, while the beam is 4 in. long.

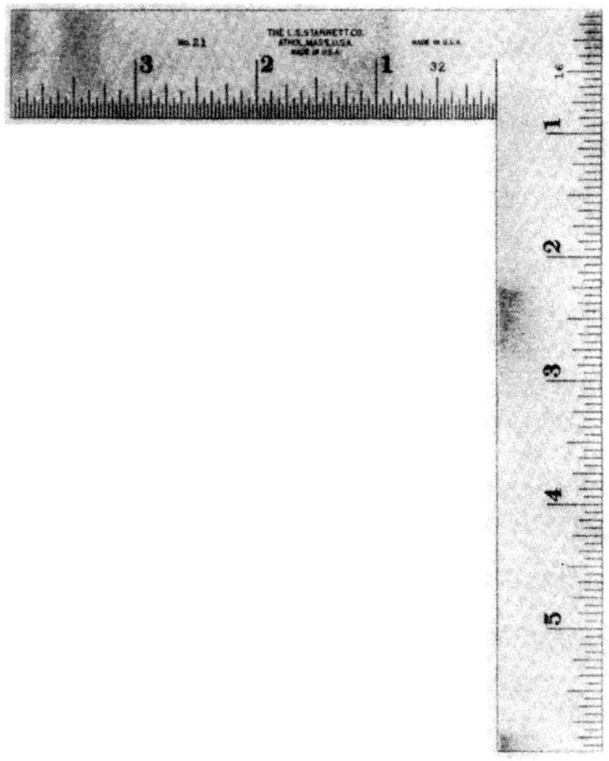

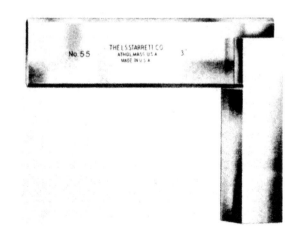

Fig. 3-3   *Thin steel try square. (Courtesy of The L. S. Starrett Company)*

Fig. 3-4   *Precision bevel edge square. (Courtesy of The L. S. Starrett Company)*

Precision Bevel Edge Square — This square is a smaller version of the machinist's try square, except that the blade is beveled on both edges to provide contact with the workpiece, as shown in Fig. 3-4. The beveled edge provides a very fine line of contact which permits greater visual accuracy than the basic combination square. A typical use of the bevel edge square would be to check a block of about 3″ for squareness or flatness to within ± .0005″.

Double Square — This square (see Fig. 3-5) is used by toolmakers and pattern makers, as well as machinists. The 6 in. blade is held fast to the

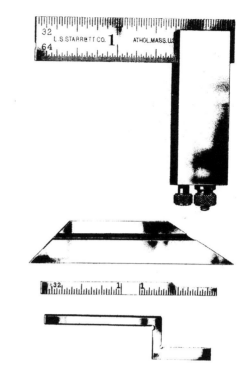

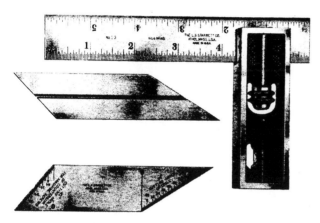

Fig. 3-5   Double square with alternate graduated and bevel blades. (Courtesy of The L. S. Starrett Company)

beam by a bolt and nut that permit the blade to be adjusted by sliding to the left or to the right, or to be replaced with the alternate blades shown, which are designed for special purposes.

Diemaker's Square — This square, shown in Fig. 3-6, is similar to the double square. Its sliding blades can be adjusted at an angle with the beam to measure the clearance in dies. The larger knurled thumb screw locks the blades at any position, whereas the smaller thumb screw tilts the blades at an angle.

To set the blades at an angle, you release the blade thumb screw and tilt the blade to the desired angle by turning the smaller thumb screw into the beam. The blade is held in position by tightening the larger thumb screw.

The *standard blade* attached to the beam is 2½ in. long (63.5mm) and ½ in. wide. It is graduated on one side, the upper edge in 32nds, and the lower edge in 64th.

Fig. 3-6   Diemaker's square and alternate blades. (Courtesy of The L. S. Starrett Company)

As shown, this square also has alternate blades that are used for special purposes.

The *bevel blade* has standard angles ground and beveled at each end: 30 deg on one end, 45 deg on the other.

The *narrow graduated blade* is 2¼ in. long (58mm) graduated in 32nds on one side, and 64ths on the other. It is $5/32$ in. wide over a length of approximately 1⅝ in., and then cut away at one end to a width of $3/32$ in.

The *offset blade* is used in situations where it is impossible to sight a straight blade. The offset blade protrudes from the square about 1½ in. and is ⅛ in. wide. Both sides of each edge are beveled to permit a line contact.

Another type of diemaker's square, shown in Fig. 3-7, is used by tool and diemakers for measuring die tapers, and by patternmakers to check angles and drafts on patterns. The beam of this square is graduated to show the angular setting of the blades in degrees. The blades can be set for any angle up to 10 deg on either side of zero. The angle is indicated by the line on the pointer.

The *narrow graduated blade* is 2¼ in. long with graduations of 32nds on one side and 64ths

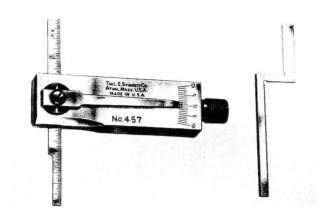

Fig. 3-7   Diemaker's square with offset blade. (Courtesy of The L. S. Starrett Company)

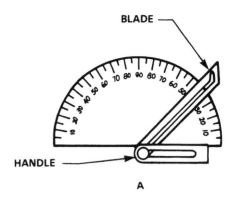

A

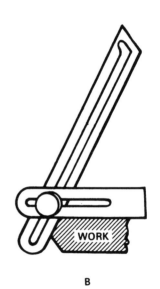

B

Fig. 3-9   Adjusting the sliding T-bevel square (A), and testing a bevel or chamfer with the sliding T-bevel square (B).

on the other. It is ⁵/₃₂ in. wide over a length of approximately 1⁵/₈ in., and then cut away at one end to a width of ³/₃₂ in.

The *offset blade*, which is used in situations where it is impossible to insert the straight blade, protrudes from the square about 1¹/₂ in.

Sliding T-Bevel Adjustable Square — The sliding T-bevel, shown in Fig. 3-8, is an adjustable try square with a slotted beveled blade that is 6 to 8 in. long. The sliding T-bevel is used for laying out and checking angles other than right angles, and for testing constructed angles, such as bevels. Because it does not have a graduated scale, the desired angle must be set with a protractor.

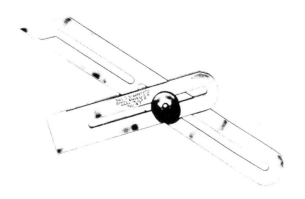

Fig. 3-8   Sliding T-bevel adjustable try square. (Courtesy of The L. S. Starrett Company)

To adjust a sliding T-bevel square to the desired angle, first loosen the thumb screw just enough to permit the blade to slide along its slot and to rotate with slight friction. Then hold the handle of the bevel against the center of the protractor, as shown in Fig. 3-9A, with its blade passing through the graduation selected. To test a bevel or chamfer for trueness, set the T-bevel square to the required angle, and hold the blade and handle to the workpiece, as shown in Fig. 3-9B. Face a source of light, and pass the blade along the length of the surface. If light shows between the blade and the surface of the workpiece, the angle is not correct. Testing the trueness of a chamfer is accomplished in the same way.

Fig. 3-10   Cylindrical square shows amount of "out-of-squareness" at a glance. (Courtesy of Brown & Sharpe Manufacturing Company)

Cylindrical Square

The cylindrical square (see Fig. 3-10) is not a square at all, but a precisely calibrated cylinder that gives direct readings of how much a workpiece is "out of square." One circular end of the true cylinder is lapped perfectly square to the axis of the cylinder, whereas the other end is lapped "out of square" to a predetermined degree. When the cylinder square is placed on its "out of square" end on a surface plate and rotated against a workpiece, its angle with the surface plate will—at some point—match the angle of the workpiece, and shut out light against the work. You then read the amount of out-of-squareness directly in 0.0002 in. by following the topmost dotted curve that is in contact with the workpiece to its reading at the top of the cylinder.

Master Squareness Gage

The master squareness gage, shown in Fig. 3-11, consists of a column with very precise vertical ways which permit a dial test indicator (or other probe) to be moved in an accurate vertical line of travel when the squareness gage and the part being checked are both placed on a surface plate (for more on surface plates and dial indicators, see Chapters V and VI). The accuracy of this type of master squareness gage is on the order of .000050 in. over 12 in. of travel. The advantage of this type of squareness gage over hand-held visual squares is that the dial test indicator allows you to read the exact amount of error

Fig. 3-11   Master squareness gage being used to check the squareness of a ground die block within .0002 in.

(out-of-squareness) instead of having to judge it visually. The master squareness gage enables you to measure squareness tolerances of .0001 in. easily.

Combination Square

The combination set, shown in Fig. 3-13, consists of four adjustable units: a square and miter head, a protractor head, a center head, and a steel rule, that is also known as the *blade*. The blade is the basic unit of the set, and has a scale that is graduated to $\frac{1}{64}$ in. When attached to the blade, any of the other three units slide along it, and can be clamped rigidly in any desired location. Other combination sets are available graduated in metric units.

The *square and miter head* forms either 90 or 45 deg angles. When the square and miter head is

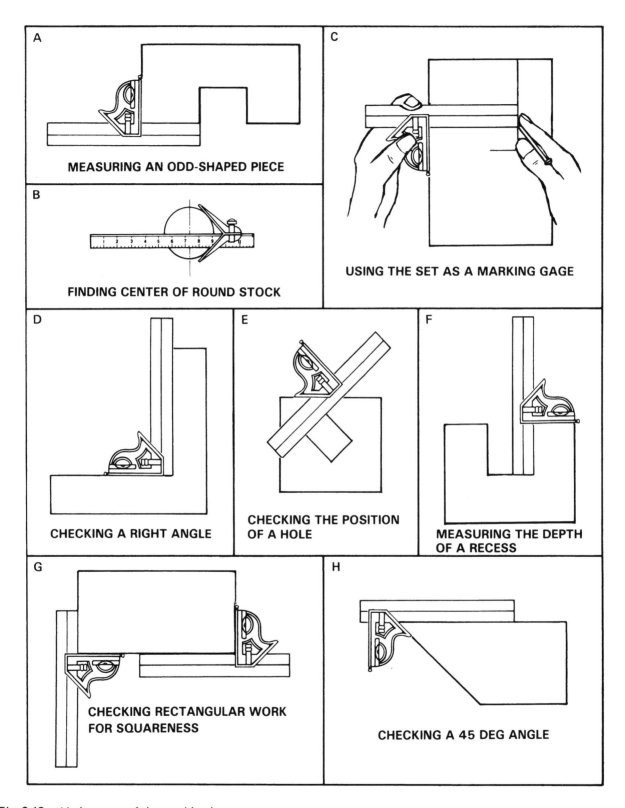

Fig. 3-12   Various uses of the combination square.

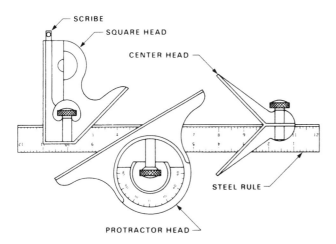

Fig. 3-13   Combination set.

attached to the blade, the arrangement is called a *combination square*. This instrument is much more versatile than a try square, because it can be used as a try square, a miter square, a spirit level, an angle gage, and a depth gage, as shown in Fig. 3-12.

The *blade* has a central groove located on its reverse side that permits the square head to be moved to any desired setting and locked in that position. The central groove is shown in each view of the blade in Fig. 3-12. The steel blade is usually graduated in eighths, sixteenths, thirty-seconds, and sixty-fourths of an inch.

In each of the uses of the combination square in Fig. 3-12, the square and miter head has been moved to the desired position on the blade and locked at that position with a reversible bolt that permits either side of the blade to be used. The knurled tip on the bolt allows it to be reversed without removing it from the head.

Another convenient feature of the square and miter head is the *spirit level*, because it is often necessary to square one piece with another and, at the same time, tell whether one or the other is level or plumb. Or, the square and miter head can also be used as a simple level. A small scriber is contained in the square and miter head, which is easily removed for use in marking (scribing) lines on metal.

The *center head* is often included as part of the combination square. It provides a fast way to locate the center of cylindrical objects by, first, clamping the center head to the blade, and then

placing the V-shaped opening snugly against the work as shown in Fig. 3-12B.

You will learn more about the *protractor head* and its use in measuring or laying out angles other than 45 deg or 90 deg later in this chapter under "Protractors."

Care of Squares

Squares are much more delicate than they look, and are subject to dents, nicks, and scratches that can spoil their accuracy. Make certain that blades, beams, heads, and all accessories are kept clean. Apply a light coat of oil to all metal surfaces to prevent corrosion when not in use. Do not use squares for purposes other than those intended. When storing squares or bevels for long periods of time, apply a liberal amount of oil or rust-preventive compound to all surfaces, wrap them in oiled paper or cloth, and place them in containers or on racks away from other tools.

SPIRIT LEVELS

Whereas squares are used to verify perpendicular angles, spirit levels are instruments designed to inspect the horizontal position of flat or cylindrical surfaces, as well as measure the direction and magnitude of minor deviations from the horizontal. Levels of varying accuracy are used in different applications. Some levels are calibrated to indicate the angle inclination of a surface in relation to a horizontal surface in degrees, minutes, and seconds. These are called *precision levels*.

The precision level shown in Fig. 3-14 is typical, although others may be longer or shorter.

Fig. 3-14   Precision spirit level. (Courtesy of Brown & Sharpe Manufacturing Company)

They range in length from 6 to 12 in. All levels have one or more glass vials, which are tubular in shape, ground to a slight arc, and closed at both ends. They contain a fluid (usually alcohol or ether) and a bubble of air. When held horizontally, the bubble will move to the highest point of the arc (center) of the vial. The glass is etched (marked) at this point. When the air bubble is centered between the etched marks, the surface is said to be level. The vial is mounted accurately in a frame, which is made from cast iron, aluminum, or steel.

Levels must be checked periodically for accuracy. To do this, first place the level on a true surface, such as a surface plate, and note the vial indication. Then, reverse the level end-for-end. If the bubble appears at a given relative position on one side of a graduation in the first reading, and at that same relative position on the other side after you have reversed it, the level is true.

Do not drop or handle a level roughly. To prevent damage, store it in a rack or other protected place when not in use.

PROTRACTORS

A protractor is an instrument used to measure the magnitude or size of angles other than 90 deg. Although some protractors are made from plastic, a protractor used in the shop should be made from steel. The main types of protractors you will use are the plane, bevel, and universal bevel with vernier.

Plane Protractors

These protractors (see Fig. 3-15) consist of a steel semicircle to which a 6 in. blade is attached by a lock joint and a thumbscrew. Angles from zero to 180 deg are etched into the steel. To measure an angle, place the bottom flat edge of the protractor along one line of the angle, and the edge of the blade against the other. Take the reading where the line marked on the blade crosses the scale. You will use the plane protractor for setting bevels, transferring angles, checking the clearance on cutters within certain limits, and many other applications.

Fig. 3-15 Plane steel protractor. (Courtesy of The L. S. Starrett Company)

Combination Set Bevel Protractor

The turret protractor head that is part of the combination set (see Fig. 3-13) is commonly called the *bevel protractor*. When attached to the blade, it can be adjusted to any position on its scale, and turned and locked at any desired angle. Angular graduations usually read from zero to 180 degrees in both directions, allowing the supplement of the angle to be read as well. A spirit level is included on some models that forms, in effect, an adjustable level to show any required degree.

You can use the bevel protractor to measure and duplicate angles. To set a specific angle on the bevel protractor, loosen the locking screw, and rotate the index mark to the desired graduation on the protractor scale. Hold this angle by tightening the locking screw.

You can also use the bevel protractor to measure existing angles on a workpiece. Simply loosen the locking screw, and align the edge of the blade with one surface on the workpiece, and align the straight edge of the bevel protractor head with the second surface on the workpiece. Tighten the locking screw. The magnitude of the angle between the two surfaces is indicated on the protractor scale at the index mark.

Universal Bevel Protractor

Plane protractors and the combination set bevel protractor only discriminate to whole degrees. The universal bevel protractor, on the other hand, discriminates to 5 min or $1/12$ deg. As shown in Fig. 3-16, this protractor consists of a round body with a fixed blade on which a turret rotates, graduated in degrees. The turret is slotted to accommodate a 7 or 12 in. non-graduated blade,

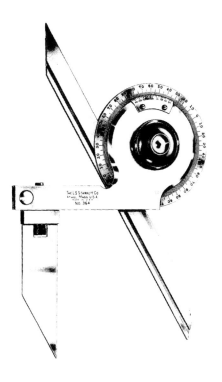

Fig. 3-16   Universal bevel protractor. (Courtesy of The
L. S. Starrett Company)

which rotates with the turret to the desired angle, and can be adjusted to the required length with a locking mechanism. The greater degree of accuracy of the universal bevel protractor is provided by a vernier scale fastened to the turret scale.

You learned how to read vernier scales in the previous chapter. Therefore, it should be easy for you to learn to read the universal bevel protractor scale, because the same vernier principle is used. The basic difference is that the turret scale on the protractor is laid out in the form of a circle, and graduated into 360 divisions of 1 deg each. This scale is also divided into four quadrants of 90 deg each, numbered from zero to 90 so that there are two zeroes and two 90 deg positions on the scale. All angles measured are referenced to the 180 deg angle of the base.

For example, if one side of the blade makes an angle of 60 deg, the other side of the blade will make the supplement of 60 deg, which is 120 deg (60 + 120 = 180). To determine which side of the blade represents the reading you want, simply observe the angle. If it is an acute angle (less than 90 deg), read the side of the blade that represents

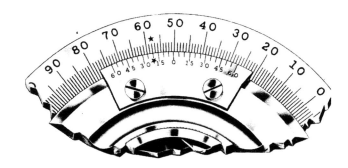

Fig. 3-17   A vernier scale on a universal bevel protractor.
(Courtesy of The L. S. Starrett Company)

an acute angle. If the angle is an obtuse angle (more than 90 deg) read the side of the blade that represents the obtuse angle.

Always read the vernier scale in the same direction from zero that you read the turret scale. The vernier scale (see Fig. 3-17) has a zero line in the center and 12 graduations on each side. The scale consists of 60 min on each side of the zero index. Each graduation represents 5 min. Every third graduation is marked by a number: 15, 30, 45, and 60. When you read the vernier scale, the zero graduation is the reference point. If the zero graduation aligns with a degree graduation on the turret scale, you need not use the vernier scale. You simply read the angle directly from the turret scale.

However, if the zero graduation on the vernier scale does not align with a degree mark, you read the minutes from the vernier scale *in the same direction from zero that you read the turret scale.* Otherwise, you will read the supplementary instead of the actual angle you are measuring. This is especially true of angles approaching 45 deg.

On the universal bevel protractor, 12 graduations on the vernier scale equal the same space as 23 graduations or 23 deg on the turret scale. Each vernier graduation is 5 min shorter than 2 graduations on the protractor dial. When the zero graduation on the vernier scale matches a graduation on the protractor scale, the reading is in exact degrees. When some other vernier graduation matches a protractor graduation, multiply the number of vernier graduations by 5 min and add the result to the total number of degrees read between the zero on the turret dial and the zero on the vernier scale.

Some universal bevel protractors are equipped with an acute angle attachment. This permits a longer line of contact on workpieces that have small angles. Generally, the acute angle attachment is used for measuring angles less than 30 deg. For example, suppose you want to check an angle of 18 deg 15 min. The reference plane would be the acute angle attachment. The reading on the protractor scale is then the supplement of the angle between the attachment and the blade.

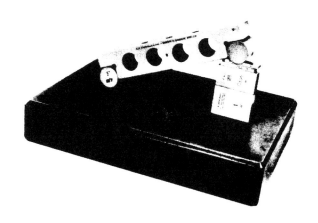

Fig. 3-18   A sine bar and precision gage blocks on a surface plate. (Courtesy of Brown & Sharpe Manufacturing Company)

SINE BARS AND SINE PLATES

A sine bar is a precisely-ground and lapped tool steel bar attached to two steel cylinders of equal diameter, used to make very accurate angle measurements, or for locating work at a given angle. A typical setup for using a sine bar is shown in Fig. 3-18. The center-to-center distance between the steel cylinders is precise. The 5 in. is the most common, but other sizes are available. The bar itself has accurately machined parallel sides, and the axes of the two cylinders are parallel to the adjacent sides of the bar within a close tolerance. Equally close tolerances control the cylinder's roundness and freedom from taper. Slots and holes are provided in the bar for convenient clamping of workpieces to the bar. Although the bar illustrated

is typical, sine bars are available in a wide variety of specialized shapes, widths, and thicknesses.

The sine bar is very easy to set up and use. However, you do need a basic knowledge of trigonometry to understand how it works. When a sine bar is set up, it always forms a *right* triangle. Remember that a right triangle has one 90 deg angle. The base of the triangle—or side adjacent—formed by the sine bar is the surface plate, as shown in Fig. 3-19. The side opposite is made up of the gage blocks that raise one end of the sine bar. The hypotenuse is always formed by the sine bar.

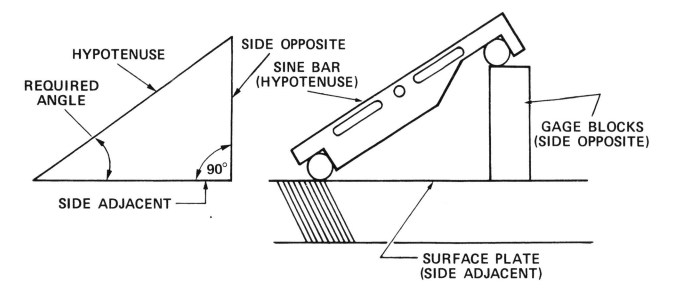

Fig. 3-19   Using a sine bar.

You can find the height of the gage block setting in either of two ways. The first method is to multiply the sine of the angle required by the length of the sine bar. The sine of the angle can be found in any table of natural trigonometric functions published in the standard reference handbooks, or by using an electronic calculator.

The second method is to use a table of sine bar constants. For example, if you had to set a 10 in. sine bar to check a 30° 5′ angle on a part, you would first refer to a table of natural trigonometric functions and find the sine of 30° 5′, which is 0.50126. Then, multiplying 0.50126 by 10 in. would give you the height of the gage blocks (0.50126 × 10 = 5.0126 in.).

Care of Sine Bars

Although sine bars have the appearance of being rugged, they are precision instruments and should receive the same care as gage blocks. Because of their use in conjunction with other tools or parts that are heavy, they are subject to rough usage. Any scratches, nicks or burrs should be removed or repaired. Sine bars should be kept clean from abrasive dirt, perspiration, and other corrosive agents. Regular inspection of the sine bar will locate such defects before they can affect its accuracy. Periodically the sine bar should be checked against precision angle gage blocks at different angle settings. Also check for wear on the cylinders and for flatness of the datum. When they are stored for extended periods, all bare metal surfaces should be cleaned and then covered with a light film of oil. Placing a cover over the sine bar and surface plate when not in use will further prevent accidental damage and discourage corrosion.

Sine Plates

Sine plates are used and cared for in the same way as sine bars, but sine plates are wider than sine bars, and contain an integral base and tapped holes for attaching a workpiece, as shown in Fig. 3-20. Their increased width allows another sine plate to be placed on top to generate compound angles. Sine plates are either hinged on one end, called *simple*, (see Fig. 3-20A), or hinged on both the side and the end, called *compound* (see Fig. 3-20B). The latter arrangement allows work to be set in two planes.

For holding work at precise angles without clamping during surface grinding or inspection, sine plates are available with a magnetic-top surface (see Fig. 3-20C). The permanent-magnet surface switches ON or OFF at the turn of a lever, yet requires no electrical connections.

Setting Simple Sine Plates. To measure an angle or to locate work to a given angle, refer to the tables of sine constants in standard reference handbooks or furnished with the sine plate to determine the corresponding distance that one end of the sine plate must be raised vertically from the true surface to obtain a desired angle. Or, refer to trigonometric function tables to find the sine of the desired angle, and multiply it by 5 when using a 5 in. sine plate, or by 10 for a 10 in. sine plate.

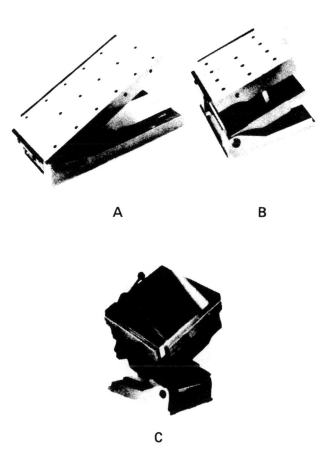

A   **B**

C

Fig. 3-20   Simple sine plate (A), compound sine plate (B), and magnetic sine plate (C). (Courtesy of Brown & Sharpe Manufacturing Company)

Setting Compound Sine Plates. When setting two known angles at 90 deg to one another, for example when the first angle = 20 deg and the second angle = 30 deg (see Fig. 3-21A):

(1) To find the amount that the intermediate plate must be raised from the base plate (distance x in Fig. 3-21B) to obtain the first angle (20 deg):

    (a) Look up the cosine of the second angle (30 deg) and the tangent of the first angle (20 deg) in the trigonometric function tables, and multiply one by the other.

    (b) Look up the product derived from (a) under "tangents" in the trigonometric function tables, and note the sine of equal degrees.

    (c) Multiply this sine by 5 (for a 5 in. sine plate), or by 10 (for a 10 in. sine plate), which will equal the distance x that the intermediate plate must be raised.

    (d) Wring the correct gage blocks together to equal dimension x, and set them in position between the base plate and the intermediate plate.

Example:

$$\cos 30 \deg = 0.86603$$
$$\tan 20 \deg = 0.36397$$
$$0.86603 \times 0.36397 = 0.3152089391 \text{ (tan)}$$
$$\text{(tan) } 0.3152089391 = 0.3006278538 \text{ (sine)}$$
$$0.3006278538 \times 10 = 3.006$$
$$\text{(for 10 in. sine plate)}$$

Therefore, 3.006 in. equals the distance x to raise the intermediate plate.

(2) To find the amount that the top plate must be raised (distance y in Fig. 3-21C) to obtain the second angle (30 deg):

    (a) Look up the sine of the second angle (30 deg) and multiply it by 5 (for a 5 in. sine plate), or by 10 (for a 10 in. sine plate), which will equal the distance y that the top plate must be raised.

    (b) Wring the correct gage blocks together to equal dimension y, and set them in position between the intermediate plate and the top plate.

Example:

$$\text{sine of 30 deg} = 0.5000$$
$$0.5000 \times 10 = 5.000 \text{ (for 10 in. sine plate)}$$

Therefore, 5.000 in. equals the distance y to raise the top plate.

Courtesy of Brown & Sharpe Manufacturing Company

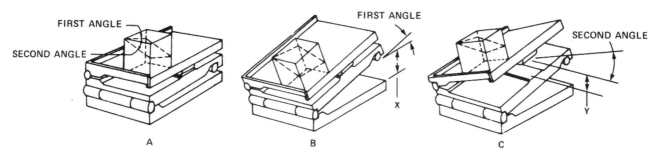

Fig. 3-21   Setting compound sine plate.

PRECISION ANGLE GAGE BLOCKS

It is much easier to construct and check small angles with precision angle gage blocks (see Fig. 3-22) than with a sine bar. Precision angle blocks used by machinists usually have an accuracy of ±1 sec (±0°0′1″), but some are manufactured to an accuracy of ±0.25 sec (±0°0′0.25″) in the laboratory or reference grade. A set of 16 precision angle blocks includes degree, minute, and second blocks that range from zero to 99 deg in 1 sec steps, and will make up to 356,400 angles (see Fig. 3-23).

The wedge shapes of all precision angle blocks have three common dimensions: the length of the base is 4 in., the width of the gaging face is 5/8 in., and the dimension at the small end is 1/4 in. The blocks are made from hardened and lapped steel. You can use angle blocks in either plus or minus positions to add to or subtract from angles.

Precision angle blocks are "wrung" together like precision gage blocks (see Chapter V), and adhere to each other in the same way.

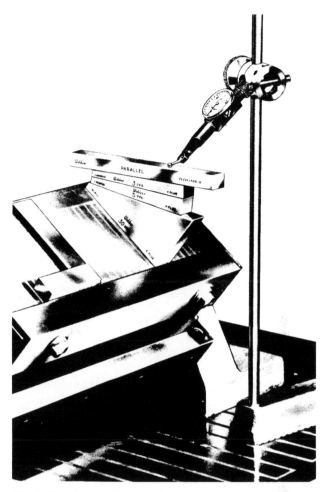

Fig. 3-22   Angle gage blocks used to set universal magnetic chuck to a precise desired angle. (Courtesy of The L. S. Starrett Company)

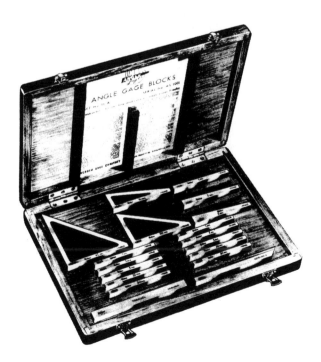

Fig. 3-23   Angle gage blocks. (Courtesy of The L. S. Starrett Company)

INDEX HEADS

Index heads (also called *indexing heads* or *dividing heads*) were originally developed to divide circles into equal divisions for such work as cutting gears, milling flutes in reamers, and milling teeth in milling cutters on milling machines. However, their use was extended to checking angles on parts revolving about a common center, because of their inherent mechanical accuracy. Although the more accurate rotary table is more often used as an inspection device, a review of index tables is included here to stress their principles of operation and use.

Applying the principles of the precision micrometer screw, the index head uses a worm and

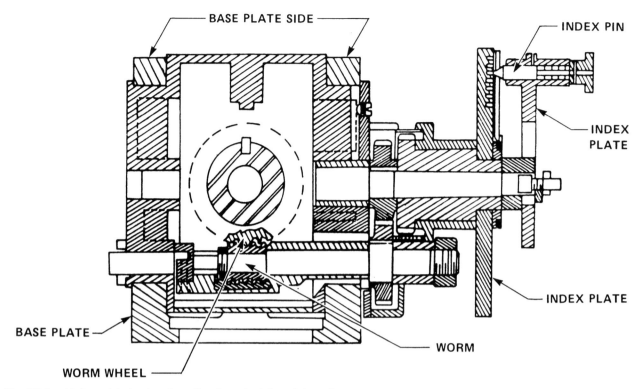

Fig. 3-24   Universal index head applies the principles of the micrometer screw.

worm wheel set (see Fig. 3-24) having a ratio of 40:1 to divide circles (360 deg) into precise equal parts. Thus, one turn of a crank turns the spindle $^{1}/_{40}$th of a revolution, or 9 deg. Index plates used with the head determine the number of divisions. For checking angles on parts having an axis of rotation-and usually an open center-the index head is used in conjunction with a surface plate. The basic parts of a universal index head are the baseplate, swivel block, spindle, index crank, and index plate all shown in Figs. 3-24 and 3-25.

The baseplate is a U-shaped casting that supports the index head on the surface plate. A large bearing in each upright of the baseplate supports the swivel block. The axis of the block is adjustable, and can be fixed at any desired angle from slightly below the horizontal position to slightly beyond the vertical position during setup. Many index heads have a vernier scale attached to their baseplates, graduated in 5 min, for very accurate swivel block positioning. The spindle extends through the swivel block, which also contains the worm and the worm wheel that rotate the spindle. The spindle is positioned at the desired

angle by means of degree graduations on the swivel block. Chucks can be mounted on the external working end of the spindle. They are usually screwed onto the spindle, or bolted directly to a flange on the spindle.

The index crank rotates the spindle. The crank is usually fastened to a shaft geared to the worm shaft. Before turning the spindle, remove the index pin from the hole in the index plate by pulling out on the index crank handle. Align the pin with the desired circle of holes by loosening the lock nut on the center shaft, shown in Fig. 3-24, and sliding the shaft along the slot in the crank. Some pins are positioned by loosening the nut on the crank, and then pivoting the portion of the crank that contains the pin.

Several index plates are usually provided with an index head. An index plate (see Fig. 3-26) is a disk that contains several concentric rings of holes. Each ring has a different number of holes. As you will see when we discuss the different types of indexing below, a difference in the number of holes is necessary to index the number of divisions required. Because the index plate is

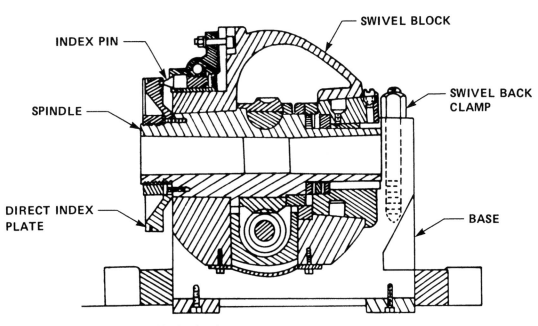

Fig. 3-25   Sectional view of a universal index head.

located behind the index crank, you must remove the crank before exchanging one index plate for another.

In normal use, the spindle must be in either the vertical or horizontal position. To align the spindle, loosen the swivel block clamps, and tilt the swivel block to the desired position. If average accuracy is permissible, you can use the degree graduations on the swivel block to position the swivel block. When a higher degree of accuracy is required, you can use a dial test indicator (described in Chapter VI).

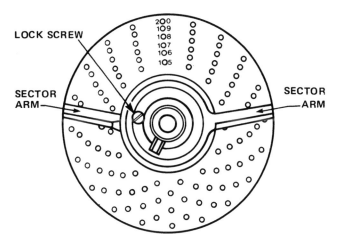

Fig. 3-26   Typical index plate.

Types of Indexing

Direct, plain, differential, and degree are the primary types of indexing. The type used will depend upon the number of divisions required, and the method that you use to measure the spacing between the divisions.

Direct Indexing — Direct indexing is the simplest means of dividing a workpiece into a required number of equal divisions. To do so, you use an index plate, such as the one shown in Fig. 3-27, to divide the work. This plate has 24 evenly-spaced holes to index any number of divisions that can be divided evenly into 24; for example, 2, 3, 4, or 6. Dividing 24 by the number of divisions desired gives the number of holes that you should rotate the spindle. (Do not count the hole that the pin is in when you begin counting.)

The direct index plate is usually located immediately behind the chuck, or is a part of the spindle. A special index pin is used for direct indexing; therefore, you do not use the index pin on the crank. Simply rotate the work until the correct hole is aligned with the index pin. Most index heads have a provision for disengaging the worm and worm wheel so that the work and spindle can be rotated by hand.

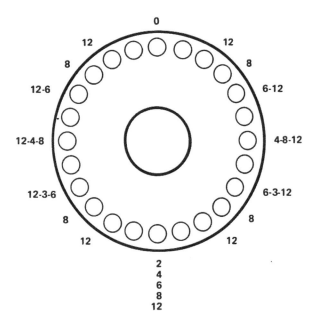

Fig. 3-27   Direct indexing plate.

Plain Indexing — Plain indexing is used when direct indexing will not provide the required number of divisions. In plain indexing, you rotate the work by turning the index crank. The ratio between the crank and the spindle is usually 40:1. This means that the work rotates $1/40$th of a turn for each full turn of the index crank, or—stated another way—it requires 40 turns of the index crank to rotate the work one complete revolution. Therefore, to determine the number of revolutions of the index crank, divide 40 by the number of divisions required.

For example, to divide the work into 2 divisions you would have to rotate the index crank 20 full turns; to obtain 4 divisions, 10 full turns, etc. If a fraction remains after you have divided 40 by the number of required divisions, the numerator of the fraction gives the number of holes to use, and the denominator gives the number of holes in the hole circle that you must move the index crank to rotate a portion (fraction) of a turn. Suppose that you are checking a hexagonal part (six sides) using plain indexing. First, you would divide 40 by 6 and get $6^4/6$ turns of the crank. If the index plate you are using has a six-hole circle, you can simply move the crank $4/6$ of a turn by moving it four holes in the six-hole circle.

If the index plate does not have a six-hole circle, however, change the fraction to an equivalent fraction that has a denominator equal to an available hole circle—either in the index plate you have on the head or another one. Thus, if a 24-hole circle is available on the plate you have on the head, you can obtain the $4/6$ turn by moving the crank 16 holes in the 24-hole circle: $4/6 \times 4 = {}^{16}/24$. When you are sure that none of the hole circles on the index plate already mounted on the index head are suitable for your use, you will have to exchange that plate for another that does.

The sector, shown in Fig. 3-26, is a time-saving device that eliminates the need to count holes for each division. Simply adjust the sector so that the index pin and the required number of holes are located between the beveled sides of the sector arms. Then, lock the arms at the desired setting by tightening the setscrew. Next, position the enclosed section by moving it in the direction of crank rotation until one sector arm contacts the index pin. After turning the index crank the required number of full turns, continue turning the index crank until the index pin is positioned next to the second sector arm.

Differential Indexing — Differential indexing is used to obtain divisions that cannot be obtained by either of the simpler indexing methods described above. The differential index head has two index plates and two index cranks. The small index pin crank is geared so that it requires 160 revolutions to equal one revolution of the large index crank. The large index crank requires 40 revolutions to rotate the work one full turn; therefore, one complete turn of the large crank equals 40 divisions. If a 100-hole circle is used, one hole on the large index plate equals $1/4000$th revolution.

To determine the required number of turns of the large and small index cranks, divide 400,000 by the number of divisions desired. The first two digits of the quotient indicate the number of holes on the large index plate, and the next two digits equal the number of holes on the small index plate—if 100-hole circles are used for both of them.

If fewer than 40 divisions are indexed, a five-digit quotient will result. The first digit of the five digit quotient equals the number of full revolutions of the large index crank. If a fraction remains after the division, divide 1 by the fraction and add one hole to the indexing movement of the small crank at intervals equal to the whole number nearest the result of the division. You will not be able to compensate entirely for the remaining fraction, but the error resulting from one hole on a 100-hole circle on the small index plate is only 0.0000942 in. on a 12 in. diameter.

The following example will help you understand how to perform differential indexing.

Example: How would you index 67 divisions, using differential indexing?

$$400,000 \div 67 = 5970 \text{ and } {}^{10}/_{67}$$

First, set the sector on the large index plate to obtain 59 spaces on the 100-hole circle, and the sector on the small index plate to obtain 70 holes on the 100-hole circle. Next, for each division, move the large index crank 59 holes, and the small index crank 70 holes in the same direction. Finally, compensate for the fraction ${}^{10}/_{67}$ ths by adding 1 hole on the small index plate every 7th division, because the nearest whole number that you obtain by dividing 1 by ${}^{10}/_{67}$ is 7.

Degree Indexing – Degree indexing is used when the spacing between holes or surfaces is given in degrees rather than in number of divisions. You can use direct, plain, or differential indexing to index by degrees.

Use direct indexing when the number of degrees desired can be divided into 360 deg exactly, and when the quotient you obtain can be divided into the number of holes on the direct indexing plate. For example, to divide the work into 30 deg divisions, divide 360 deg by 30. The quotient, 12, indicates that you must divide the work into 12 divisions that are 30 deg apart. Now, divide 24 (the number of holes on the direct index plate) by 12 (the number of divisions). The quotient, 2, indicates the number of holes that you must use to index 30 deg on the direct index plate.

2 holes in an 18-hole circle index work 1°		
1	27	$1/3°$
6	54	$1°$
4	54	$2/3°$
3	54	$1/2°$
2	54	$1/3°$

Fig. 3-28   Index plate selection guide.

When dividing work into degrees by plain indexing, remember that one turn of the index crank will rotate the work $1/40$ th of a revolution. Since one revolution of the work equals 360 deg, one turn of the index crank would revolve the work $1/40$ th of 360 deg, or 9 deg. Therefore, $1/9$ of a turn of the index crank would revolve or index the work 1 deg. Use Fig. 3-28 to help you select a dividing head index plate for degree indexing a workpiece.

To determine the number of revolutions and parts of a revolution to turn the index crank to index work the desired number of degrees, divide the number of degrees to be indexed by 9. The quotient will represent the number of complete turns and fraction of a turn that you must rotate the index crank. Set the sector arms for the number of holes that will give the desired fraction of a turn.

The calculation for indexing work 15 deg using an index plate having a 54-hole circle is:

$$15 \div 9 = 1^{6}/_{9} = 1^{36}/_{54}$$

or one complete turn of the index crank and 36 holes in a 54-hole circle.

The calculation for indexing work $13\frac{1}{2}$ deg using the 18-hole circle of an index plate is:

$$\frac{13\frac{1}{2}}{9} \times \frac{2}{2} = {}^{27}/_{18} = 1^{9}/_{18}$$

or one complete turn and 9 holes in an 18-hole circle.

When indexing angles given in minutes—and providing that approximate divisions are acceptable—you can determine the rotation of the index crank and proper index plate by the following method:

Determine the number of minutes represented by one turn of the index crank by multiplying the number of degrees covered in one turn of the index crank by 60. If one turn represents 9 deg, the number of minutes represented by one turn of the index crank is 540 (9 × 60 = 540). Therefore, 540 divided by the number of minutes in the division desired represents the number of holes in the index plate circle. Move the index crank one hole on the index plate to obtain the required division in minutes.

As mentioned previously, you can use this method of indexing only for approximate angles, because the quotient will usually come out in mixed numbers, or in numbers for which no index plates are available. However, when the quotient is nearly equal to the number of holes in an available index plate, you can use the nearest number of holes, because the error will be very small. For example, the calculation for 24 min is:

$$\frac{540}{24} = 22.5$$

Since there is no 22.5-hole circle on the index plate, you would use a 23-hole circle plate.

On the other hand, if the quotient is *not* almost equal to an available circle of holes, multiply it by a trial number, which may give a product equal to the number of holes in one of the available index circles. You can then move the crank the required number of holes to give the desired division. For example, the calculation for determining 54 min when an index plate having a 20-hole circle is available is:

$$\frac{540}{54} = \frac{10}{1} \times \frac{2}{2} = \frac{20}{2}$$

or 2 holes in a 20-hole circle index plate.

You can also index an angle in degrees, minutes, and seconds using a differential index head. On the large plate, one complete turn of the large crank equals 9 deg, six spaces in the 54-hole circle equals 1 deg, and one space in the 54-hole circle equals 10 min. On the small plate, ten spaces in the 54-hole circle equals 1 min, and one space in the 54-hole circle equals 6 sec. For example, to index an angle of 3°20'12":

(1) Change the number of degrees and minutes to minutes (200).

(2) Divide the number of minutes by 10. The quotient gives the sector setting on the 54-hole circle of the large index plate (20 spaces).

(3) Divide the number of seconds, 12, by 6. The quotient gives the sector setting on the 54-hole circle of the small index plate (2 spaces).

(4) Index the large crank an amount equal to the sector setting, which is 20 spaces.

(5) Index the small crank an amount equal to the sector setting, which is 2 spaces. The indexing results in an angle of 3°20'12"

ROTARY TABLES

A more precise way to generate and measure angles on parts is by using a rotary table. The three categories of rotary tables are (1) optical, (2) mechanical cam-compensated, and (3) mechanical worm and gear.

Optical Rotary Table

One type of optical rotary table (see Fig. 3-29) incorporates a microscope that reads a precision circular scale, which is the angle measuring element. Another optical rotary table employs Moire fringe averaging of the circular graduations. Both types have similar operating characteristics.

The number of graduations around the main or master circular scale of an optical rotary table like the one shown in Fig. 3-29 depends on its diameter, the width of the graduations, and the magnification of the microscope. The table is

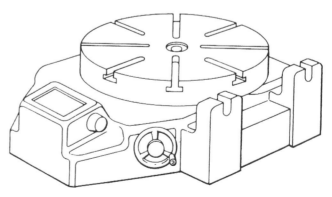

Fig. 3-29   Optical rotary table. (Courtesy of Moore Special Tool Company, Inc.)

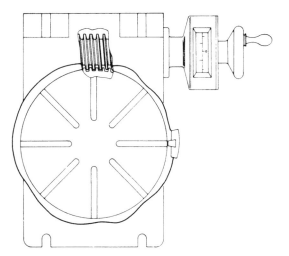

Fig. 3-30   Mechanical, cam-compensated rotary table. (Courtesy of Moore Special Tool Company, Inc.)

Fig. 3-32   Rotary table with digital readout. (Courtesy of Moore Special Tool Company, Inc.)

usually graduated at intervals of $^1/_6$ or $^1/_3$ of a degree. A graduated drum or other optical vernier arrangement allows settings to be made to finer increments of minutes and seconds. In the optical rotary tables that average the graduations, the fine increments of minutes and seconds are set by a sine curve generated by either electronic or optical pulsing. A worm and gear serves to displace the table to positions established by the optical system.

Mechanical Cam-Compensated Rotary Table

The accuracy of this type of rotary table, shown in Fig. 3-30, is directly related to the accuracy of the worm and gear set. A cam,

Fig. 3-31   Mechanical worm and gear rotary table (Courtesy of Moore Special Tool Company, Inc.)

attached to the rotary table, is used to compensate for any gear error. The shape of the cam is determined by the calibrated error of the rotary table. A follower, which works against the cam, either advances or reverses the vernier dial to match the error of the gear at a particular angle.

Mechanical Worm and Gear Rotary Table

The very accuracy worm and the gear used in this type of rotary table (see Fig. 3-31) do not require any corrective mechanism, such as a cam or other means to compensate for error in normal use. Instead, the gear and worm is machined and lapped to final accuracy.

You can set an angle on this rotary table in several ways, using

(1)   The precision worm shaft vernier dial,

(2)   An index plate fixed to the worm shaft dial housing in a manner similar to that used with the index head,

(3)   A digital readout (see Fig. 3-32) interfaced with the precision worm and gear drive (the readout can be set to display angular position in terms of degrees, minutes, and seconds, *or degrees and decimal degrees* (0.001 deg increments),

(4)   A stepping motor drive interfaced with a manually-set controller for automatic positioning at the operator's command, and

(5)   The rotary table interfaced with a numerical control system for fully automatic programable control of angular position.

CHAPTER III REVIEW

1.   A try square has been dropped sharply upon the floor. How would you check for damage?

2.   Determine the correct height settings for a 5″ sine bar to give the following angles:

a)   15° 30′   c)   25° 15′   e)   41.25°

b)   62°   d)   8.5°   f)   47° 30′15″

3.   Match the various indexing methods used with index heads:

A.   Direct indexing   a)   One turn of the handwheel moves the base plate ¹/₄₀ th revolution

B.   Plain indexing   b)   Uses 2 handwheels and 2 index plates

C.   Differential indexing   c)   Division in angular measure instead of number of holes

D.   Degree indexing   d)   Divisions on base plate match those being made

4.   What device would you use to set angles in two planes?

5.   Why are index plates made with varying numbers of holes?

6.   Compute the number of turns of the index crank necessary to make the following indexes (using ¹/₄₀ revolution per index crank revolution):

a)   15°, using an 18-hole plate

b)   32°, using a 54-hole plate

c)   120°, using a 24-hole plate

d)   31.5°, using an 18-hole plate

7.   What are the angles generated by the following sine-bar elevations?

With a 5″ sine bar:

a)   5.1414   b)   3.3530   c)   2.1574   d)   4.000   e)   6.5000

With a 10″ sine bar:

f)   3.2511   g)   5.1414   h)   2.000   i)   7.1267   j)   5.9355

Chapter III Review (continued)

8.   Determine the necessary sine-bar elevations to generate the following angles:

With a 5″ sine-bar:

a)   62°   b)   35°30′   c)   29°14′   d)   10°10′50″

With a 10″ sine-bar:

e)   46°25′30″   f)   21°19′20″   g)   60°50′45″   h)   50°31′22″

9.   Find the elevation settings for the intermediate and upper plates of a compound 10″ sine plate for the following angles:

a)   22° lower, 37° upper

b)   35°20′ lower, 14°15′ upper

c)   40°20′35″ lower, 26°42′18″ upper

Chapter IV

Common Comparison Instruments and Fixed-Size Gages

As you learned in Chapter I, indirect-reading measuring instruments are not graduated in any unit of measurement. These tools are used to transfer and/or compare measurements. This means that the magnitude obtained with the instrument must be compared to a known standard of measure, or used in conjunction with another direct-reading instrument.

Most transfer and comparison measurements are made in two steps:

(1) An indirect-reading instrument is first used to determine the magnitude of an unknown distance.

(2) This magnitude is then transferred to and/or compared with another instrument that is graduated into units of measurement.

This procedure is commonly known as *indirect comparison measurement* or *transfer measurement*. The transfer of measurements, however, can reduce the reliability of a measurement by introducing error—usually human error. Keep this in mind when using indirect-reading instruments.

Purely comparison instruments are used directly as gages to determine the accuracy of part form or shape. Some examples of such gages are thickness, small hole, radius, and center gages.

STRAIGHTEDGES

Straightedges look very much like rules, except that they are not graduated. They are used primarily for checking and inspecting plane surfaces for straightness. However, they are also used as guides for drawing or scribing straight lines between two points.

Straightedges are flat lengths of tool steel or

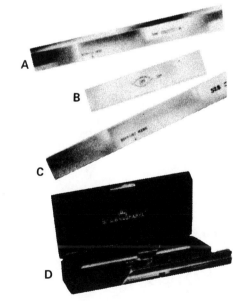

Fig. 4-1   (A) Beveled steel straightedge, (B) hardened steel straightedge, (C) standard steel straightedge, and (D) knife-edge straightedge set. (Courtesy of Brown & Sharpe Manufacturing Company)

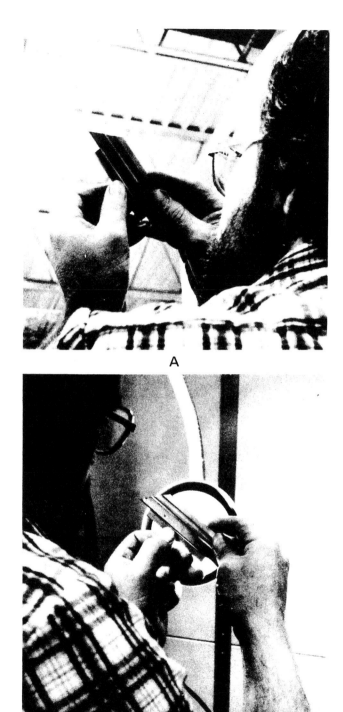

A

B

Fig. 4-2   Using the knife-edge straightedge for checking flatness. See the light showing between the part and knife-edge straightedge.

stainless steel, ground to extremely fine tolerances, particularly along their edges. They range in length approximately to 12 ft, and are available with or without a beveled edge, as shown in Fig. 4-1A, B, and C. Figure 4-1D shows a set of knife-edge straightedges designed for checking flatness to extreme accuracy. Their testing edges are very narrow and semicircular in cross section, providing a line contact that discloses minute curvatures. Holding a knife-edge straightedge and the part being measured up to a light (see Fig. 4-2), you can judge a tolerance of .0001 in. on flatness.

When using a standard steel straightedge, a thickness or feeler gage (described later in this chapter) should be used with the straightedge to check surface variations when working to close tolerances. Always keep a straightedge in a box when you are not using it. Although straightedges are made from tough steel to prevent warping and wear, do not test their edges by banging on them. Some straightedges are marked with two arrows—one near each end—that indicate balance points.

CALIPERS

The term *caliper* designates an instrument used to test the dimensions of workpieces. Calipers are commonly used to make comparison measurements when extreme accuracy is not required (less than $1/64$ in.). They are used to measure internal and external diameters and distances, and to compare distances and sizes. When designed to take inside readings, the contacts of the caliper face outward; to take outside readings, the contacts face inward. Calipers are always used with a steel rule or, sometimes with micrometers.

A large variety of calipers is available for many measuring operations in the shop. The four basic classifications of calipers are: spring joint, firm joint, lock joint, and hermaphrodite.

ADJUSTABLE PARALLELS

Adjustable parallels (see Fig. 4-3A) have a wide range of uses in layout, gaging, inspection work, and for setups on various machine tools. They are very useful as gages in checking the size of slots and parallel openings. Their adjustable feature allows them to be set to exact size by using a micrometer and also permits them to be

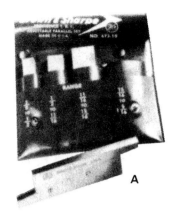

A

B

Fig. 4-3   Adjustable parallels. (Courtesy of Brown & Sharpe Manufacturing Company)

Fig. 4-4   Planer gage. (Courtesy of Brown & Sharpe Manufacturing Company)

used in place of several solid parallels or parallel blocks.

Typical adjustable parallels consist of two precision-ground wedges of steel connected on their inclined surfaces by a sliding dovetail. Lock screws are provided to adjust the clearance in the dovetail, or lock the parallels at any width between their maximum and minimum limits after setting a measurement.

To measure with parallels, first slide the halves, causing the width to increase or decrease, depending on the direction desired. Place the parallels in the groove or slot to be measured (see Fig. 4-3B), and expand them until the parallel edges conform to the width to be measured. Then, lock the parallels together with a small screwdriver, and measure their width with an outside micrometer. If possible, leave the adjustable parallels in place while you measure them.

Adjustable parallels are available in individual sizes or in sets with a range from ³/₈ to 2¹/₄ in. All parallels are ⁹/₃₂ in. thick.

PLANER GAGES

The planer gage, like the adjustable parallels described in the paragraphs above, has two inclined planes, as shown in Fig. 4-4. When the two parts are moved relative to each other, the distances between the parallel surfaces of the gage changes. You can set the distance between the surfaces to exact distances on a surface plate using a surface gage or vernier height gage using a dial test indicator with gage blocks. You can also set the gage to the finished thickness of the work with a micrometer.

The planer gage was designed primarily to save planer or shaper operators much time and effort in setting the cutting tool to the proper depth, because this gage eliminates the slow method of cut and try. With the planer gage resting upon the machine platen, you adjust the cutting tool in contact with the gage. You can then rely upon the first cut to be the proper thickness. You can also use the planer gage to check the width of slots and grooves within the limits of the gage. In addition, you can use the planer gage in conjunction with a sine bar when doing angular work.

While still a handy item in the tool box, planer gages are becoming less common with the declining use of shapers and planers.

THICKNESS GAGES

A thickness gage (often called a *feeler gage*) consists of a set of tempered steel blades fastened together like a jack knife (see Fig. 4-5), each of which is accurately ground to a different specific thickness marked on the blade in millimeters or thousandths of an inch (0.001). Each blade is ¹/₂ in. wide. The blades usually range in thickness from 0.0015 in. (about one-half the thickness of

Fig. 4-5   Thickness gages. (Courtesy of Brown & Sharpe Manufacturing Company)

a hair on your head) to 0.025 in. (about the thickness of your thumbnail). Thickness gages are useful for measuring narrow slots, setting small gaps and clearances, determining fit between mating surfaces, and for checking the flatness of parts in straightening operations. You can measure the amount of clearance between adjacent surfaces by using either a single blade or a combination of two or more blades.

When you use a combination of blades to obtain a desired gage thickness, try to place the thinner blades between the heavier ones to protect the thinner blades, and to keep them from kinking. Do not force blades into openings that are too small or the blades may bend and kink. A thickness gage is often called a feeler gage, because the accuracy of the measurement depends upon a skilled sense of touch or "feel." A good way to get the feel of using a feeler gage correctly is to practice taking measurements with the gage on openings of known dimensions.

RADIUS GAGES

Radius gages (sometimes called *fillet gages*) also consist of two sets of thin steel blades which may be fastened together like a jack knife or packed singly in a folding case (see Fig. 4-6A). Their

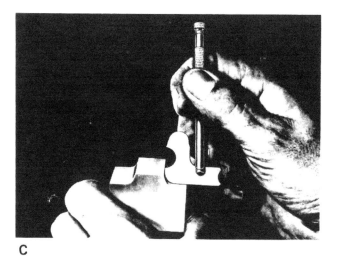

A

C

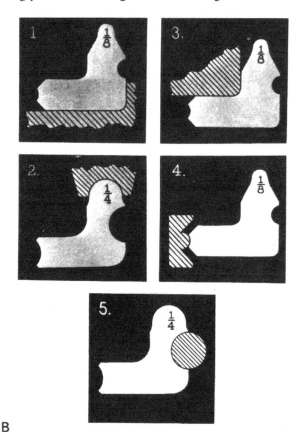

B

Fig. 4-6   Radius gages. (Courtesy of The L. S. Starrett Company)

profiles are used to check the size and accuracy of the radii of concave and convex corners and shoulders, as shown in Fig. 4-6B. Each blade fits one—and only one—inside or outside radius, and is stamped with the radius size in either English or metric units of measure. The blades increase in radius by 64ths and 32nds of an inch, or 0.5 and 1mm. Radius gages are also used as templates when grinding form cutting tools.

, To use a radius gage, simply find one that fits the radius being checked, and read the size on the face of the blade. A locking device is provided to securely hold any one of the blades in the desired position. A holder, such as the one in Fig. 4-6C, is very useful for checking radii in hard-to-reach locations. To check close tolerance radii, use an optical comparator (see Fig. 7-35).

SCREW PITCH GAGES

Screw pitch gages (sometimes called *thread pitch gages*) look somewhat like thickness and radius gages (see Fig. 4-7A). However, all of the leaves have about the same thickness, and the edge of each blade has a different number of teeth per inch cut into it, corresponding to the exact form of threads of various pitches in the different thread standards. This gage is used to determine the pitch of a screw, bolt, or other threaded unit, as shown in Fig. 4-7B. Although you can check the number of threads per inch with a rule, it is very difficult to accurately count fine pitches of screw threads. Therefore, a screw pitch gage is especially convenient for checking the finer screw threads. You can determine the pitch on a threaded unit by trying various blades until one fits perfectly. The number stamped into the blade indicates the pitch or number of threads per inch.

A

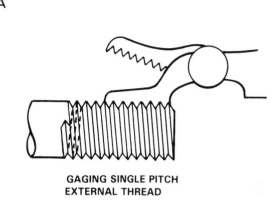

GAGING SINGLE PITCH EXTERNAL THREAD

B

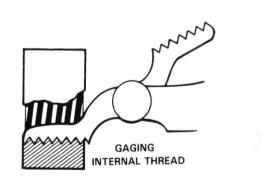

GAGING INTERNAL THREAD

Fig. 4-7   Screw pitch gages (Courtesy of Brown & Sharpe Manufacturing Company)

ACME THREAD TOOL GAGES

These gages, shown in Fig. 4-8, are used both to set and to grind the tool used in cutting Acme threads. The sides of the Acme thread tool gage have an included angle of 29 deg (14$\frac{1}{2}$ deg to a side), the angle generally used in cutting worm gears.

The Acme screw thread is used on valve stems, the lead screw of a lathe, and other threaded parts requiring a strong thread. The crest and root of the threads are similar to a square thread in that they are flat.

Fig. 4-8   Acme thread tool gage. (Courtesy of Brown & Sharpe Manufacturing Company)

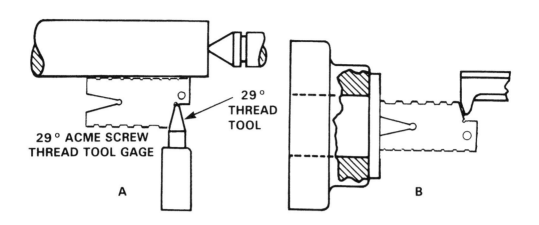

Fig. 4-9   Using an Acme thread tool gage. (Courtesy of Brown & Sharpe Manufacturing Company)

Figures 4-9A and B show how to use an Acme thread tool gage when cutting an external and internal Acme thread, respectively. Note that a 29 deg Acme thread tool gage is used in the same way as the center gage (see below) is used for 60 deg V-form screw threads. Simply adjust the cutting edge of the tool to align it exactly with the beveled edge of the gage. The notches in the Acme thread tool gage permit you to grind the squared front edge of the tool bit accurately in accordance with the pitch of the thread to be machined.

CENTER GAGES

Center gages (see Fig. 4-10A) are used primarily to check and set the angle of V-form sharp and standard tools used in thread cutting. They are also used in checking the angle of lathe centers (see Fig. 4-10B). In addition, you can use the scales stamped on them in fractions and millimeters to determine the pitch of the four most commonly used threads.

A center gage is used like the Acme thread tool gage, described above. Each notch on the side and the point of the gage has an included angle of 60 deg.

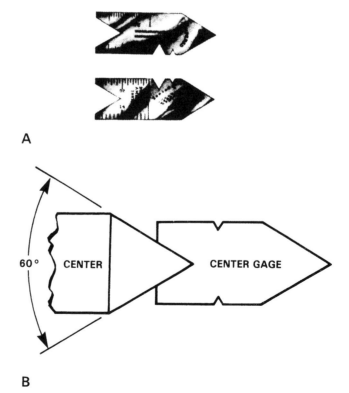

Fig. 4-10   Center gage. (Courtesy of Brown & Sharpe Manufacturing Company)

DRILL GAGES

A drill gage (see Fig. 4-11) is a flat rectangularly-shaped steel plate containing holes of various diameters, corresponding to the sizes of standard twist drills. Each hole is marked with its particular size in gage numbers, letters, fractions, or decimal equivalents. You can quickly determine the size of any small twist drill by fitting the fluted end into the drill gage holes until you find the smallest one that will allow the drill to enter. In addition, most drill gages also list information pertaining to the correct relation between drill and tap sizes for commonly-used machine screws.

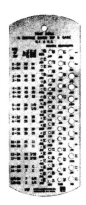

Fig. 4-11   Drill gage. (Courtesy of Brown & Sharpe Manufacturing Company)

WIRE GAGES

Wire gages, such as the one shown in Fig. 4-12, are used for measuring the diameters of wires and to determine the gage (thickness) of sheet metal. Each cutout on the outer perimeter gages a different size from No. 0 to No. 36. The larger the gage number, the smaller the diameter or thickness. Wire diameters are also expressed in thousandths of an inch (0.001), as well as by gage numbers. Gages are available for all of the common standards, including Birmingham, American, U.S. Standard, and steel wire or Washburn & Moen.

To measure wire size, use the appropriate gage as shown in Fig. 4-12. Do not try to force the wire into a slot. Find the slot that refuses to pass the wire without forcing. Then, try the next larger slot until you find one that passes the wire. That is the correct size. Remember to always take the measurement at the slot portion of the cutout, rather than the circular portion of the gage. When you have obtained the gage number, turn the gage over and read the decimal equivalent for that number.

To measure the gage of a piece of sheet metal, first remove any burrs from the spot where you intend to apply the gage. Then select the appropriate gage for the metal to be measured and apply it to the edge of the sheet metal. The number opposite the slot that fits the sheet is its gage number. You will find its decimal equivalent stamped on the opposite side of the gage.

You can make these measurements with a micrometer or vernier caliper, but the simple circular gage is less expensive, faster, and easier.

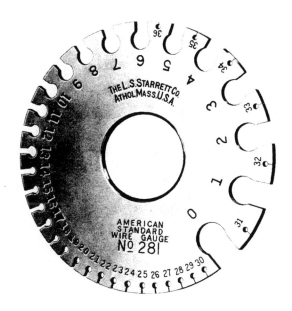

Fig. 4-12   Wire and sheet metal gage. (Courtesy of The L. S. Starrett Company)

TELESCOPING GAGES

Telescoping gages (see Fig. 4-13A) are used in conjunction with outside micrometers or vernier calipers to quickly and accurately obtain the inside measurements of slots, grooves, or holes. The T-shaped instrument is available in two styles. One consists of a handle attached to a perpendicular fixed contact, into which a contact plunger (see Fig. 4-13B) telescopes under spring tension. The

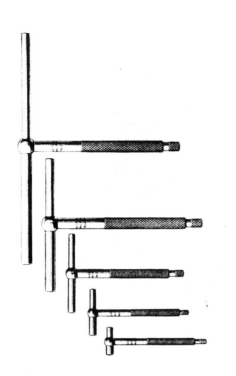

A

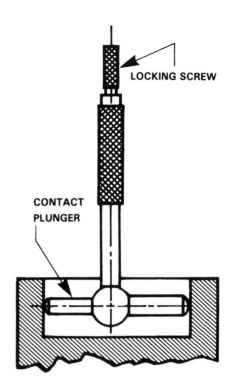

B

other style has two movable contact plungers, one telescoping into the other. In both styles, the contacts can be locked in any position by turning a knurled screw at the end of the handle, as shown in Fig. 4-13B. The telescoping gage is a transfer instrument and is therefore not calibrated, but you can read the final size by measuring over the contacts with an outside micrometer. Telescoping gages are available either singly or in sets (usually five or six), whose contacts will measure from $\frac{1}{2}$ to 6 in. in width or diameter.

To use the telescoping gage, first select the appropriate gage for the desired measurement range. Compress the plungers, and lock them in position. Then, insert the contacts into the hole to be measured (see Fig. 4-13C). As you do so, tilt one contact forward with a slight rocking motion so that the plungers can expand to the highest point of the hole diameter. Then align the handle with the centerline of the hole, and release the lock screw on the end of the handle. Rocking the gage head in the hole before releasing the lock screw is very important in making accurate measurements, especially in large diameters. Now, tighten the lock screw firmly and again tilt one contact forward

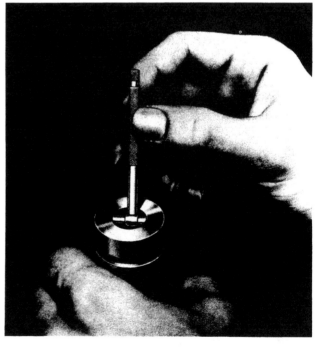

C

Fig. 4-13   Telescoping gages. (Courtesy of The L. S. Starrett Company)

to release the other contact. Finally, remove the gage carefully, and determine the exact size of the hole by measuring the distance across the two contacts with an outside micrometer. Try to obtain the same "feel" on the gage with the micrometer as you did when the gage was in contact with the hole diameter. Too much pressure exerted on the gage plungers by the micrometer spindle and anvil will cause an incorrect reading. Take at least two readings with a telescoping gage to verify your measurement. If the readings do not agree, repeat the procedure again.

SMALL HOLE GAGES

Small hole gages are used to measure slots, grooves, or recesses having widths or diameters less than ½ in. These gages are available in sets of four or more, and will measure distances of approximately 0.125 to 0.500 in. (4 to 12mm).

A small hole gage (see Fig. 4-14) is similar to the telescoping gage in construction and use, except that its contact surface consists of a small split ball mounted on the end of the handle instead of crossarms. The ball contact halves are flattened to permit their use in shallow holes and recesses.

The halves of the ball are expanded until they contact the sides of the hole by turning a knurled knob at the end of the handle. Then rock the gage handle slightly from side to side until you obtain the proper "feel" (the slight drag of the ball halves against the sides of the hole). Finally, withdraw the gage carefully, and obtain the final size by measuring over the contact halves with an outside micrometer caliper.

CUTTER CLEARANCE GAGES

A cutter clearance gage, shown in Fig. 4-15, is used to determine the correct clearance angles on milling cutters that range in diameter from 2 to 3 in. or more. The gage will measure angles ranging from zero to 30 deg. It consists of a frame graduated from zero to 30 deg with a fixed foot, an adjustable sliding foot on the beam extension of the frame, and a blade that is adjustable both angularly and perpendicularly to contact the clearance angle of the cutter tooth.

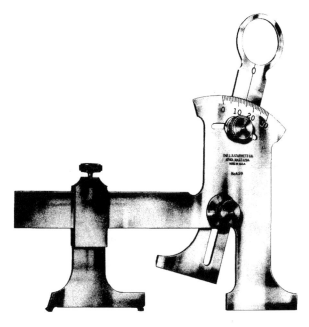

Fig. 4-15   Cutter clearance gage. (Courtesy of The L. S. Starrett Company)

To use the gage, first set the adjustable blade to the correct clearance angle. Then, position the feet on two alternate teeth of the cutter with the frame at right angles to the cutter axis. The adjustable blade will show you whether or not the cutter tooth is ground to the desired angle.

Fig. 4-14   Small hole gages (Courtesy of The L. S. Starrett Company)

This is a specialized gage used largely in tool and cutter grinding, and in shops that regularly use larger milling cutters.

FIXED-SIZE AND LIMIT GAGES

The shape of a *fixed-size gage* is the complement or reverse replica of the part whose dimensions are being measured. Such gages complement the part dimensions either in its *nominal condition* (the size exactly halfway between the limits of size), or in either of its *limiting conditions* (maximum material or least material) on the specified tolerances of the part dimensions. The latter are called *limit gages*.

Limit gages are of two kinds: (1) maximum-material-condition (MMC) gages, known as *GO gages*, which control the minimum allowable looseness or maximum allowable tightness in the fit of mating parts and thereby control interchangeability; and (2) least-material-condition (LMC) gages, known as *NOT-GO gages*—or in the cases of thread gages, *high* or *low* gages—which control the maximum looseness or minimum interference between mating parts. Thus, limit gages largely control the tightness or looseness of the assembled parts.

The use of limit gages is a fast way to determine whether or not the product is within prescribed limits. Deviation gages, described in later chapters, measure *how much* the part deviates from a nominal or a basic size.

The remainder of this chapter discusses some common types of fixed size and limit gages.

RING GAGES

Ring gages consist of cylindrical rings of steel whose internal diameters are ground, and then honed or lapped to a specified size. They are used to check the diameter of cylindrical parts, such as shafts, rods, and pins. Ring gages are usually used in pairs called *GO/NOT-GO gages*. The difference in the hole size between the two gages is equal to the tolerance of the parts being machined. If a part fits into the larger gage but not into the smaller gage, it is within tolerance. Any part that fits into the smaller gage is too small and is not acceptable. Any part that will not enter the larger ring gage is too large and must be remachined.

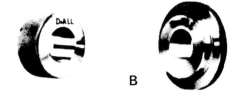

Fig. 4-16   (A) Solid ring gage; (B) Flanged ring gage. (Courtesy of DoAll Company)

The three basic designs of plain ring gages are solid, flanged, and annular. The solid type (see Fig. 4-16A) is generally used for small diameters from 0.059 to 1.510 in. The flanged type (see Fig. 4-16B) is generally used for medium diameters ranging from 1.510 to 8.010 in. They are flanged to reduce weight, increase rigidity, and facilitate handling. A solid knurled surface around the outside edge of a ring gage indicates that it is a GO gage. If there is a groove cut around the gage, in the middle of the knurled surface, it is a NOT-GO gage. The annular type is generally used for larger diameters ranging from 9.010 to 12.010 in., and is provided with handles.

To meet various tolerance conditions, both ring and plug gages (described below) are manufactured in several classes of accuracy (see Fig. 4-17) designated by XX, X, Y and Z. (XXXX and XXX are also available but not frequently required.) Of the first four levels of accuracy mentioned, XX is made to the closest gage manufacturer's tolerance. Class Z is made to the most liberal tolerance. Specific values of these tolerances are published by the major gage manufacturers. It is standard practice to select a gage that is accurate to one-tenth of the part tolerance.

Ring gages are also used as masters for setting dial bore gages and in air gaging (see Chapters VI and VII).

Size Range		CLASS XX	CLASS X	CLASS Y	CLASS Z
Above	To and Including				
.005"	.010"	.00002"	.00004"	.00007"	.00010"
.010	.029	.00002	.00004	.00007	.00010
.029	.825	.00002	.00004	.00007	.00010
.825	1.510	.00003	.00006	.00009	.00012
1.510	2.510	.00004	.00008	.00012	.00016
2.510	4.510	.00005	.00010	.00015	.00020
4.510	6.510	.000065	.00013	.00019	.00025
6.510	9.010	.00008	.00016	.00024	.00032
9.010	12.260	.00010	.00020	.00030	.00040

Fig. 4-17   Standard gagemakers tolerance chart.

RECEIVING GAGES

Receiving gages are similar to ring gages. However, receiving gages are fixed gages designed to inspect a number of dimensions and also their relationship to each other. They are called receiving gages because they resemble the cavity that receives the part in actual service. They are used to check the GO limits and contour of *noncircular* parts, such as splined shafts.

PLUG GAGES

Plug gages are cylinders of steel whose diameters are ground, then honed or lapped to a specified size. A plug gage is used to check the diameter of cylindrical cavities, such as precision holes or bearing bores. It may be round, tapered, or irregular in shape. It may have either an integral handle or a replaceable handle. Most plug gages have two ends. If a hole machined in the work is the right size, the GO end of the gage just fits in the hole, and the NOT-GO end does not. The GO end of the gage determines if the hole is too *small* and the NOT-GO end checks if it is too *large*.

A plug gage checks only the size of a hole where it enters the workpiece and does not check roundness or straightness of the hole. These are checked by the dial bore gage or a dial hole gage (refer to Chapter VI).

Notice in Fig. 4-18 how the dimensional tolerances on either end of the gage compare with the tolerances specified on the hole. Generally, the dimensional tolerances on a GO/NOT-GO gage will be approximately 10% of the dimensional tolerance of the part or feature to be checked.

The four types of plug gages are: reversible, taperlock, trilock, and progressive, as shown in Fig. 4-19. The reversible type is available in sizes ranging from 0.010 in. (0.254mm) up to 0.750 in. (19.05mm). The taperlock was the original standard type, and is still manufactured for sizes from 0.059 in. (1.5mm) to 1.510 in. (38.35mm). Above 1.510 in. (38.35mm), the trilock type is used, which consists of disks fastened to a handle. The progressive plug, which can check both GO and NOT-GO dimensions in one motion, is used primarily for convenience.

Each gage design has a GO and NOT-GO section. The GO is at the minimum tolerance limit

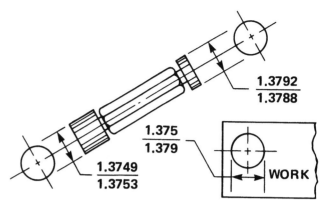

Fig. 4-18   How a plug gage is used to check specified hole dimensions.

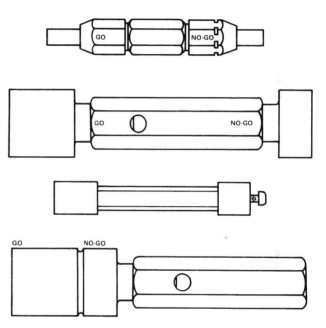

Fig. 4-19   Plug gage types: reversible, taperlock, trilock, and progressive.

and should enter the hole to be gaged. The NOT-GO is at the high limit and should not enter the hole. If the hole meets these conditions, it is within the tolerance limits.

GAGE PINS

Gage pins are frequently used when, for example, close tolerances of small hole sizes are to be checked when other types of measuring instruments would be impractical. Gage pins are commercially available in several classes of

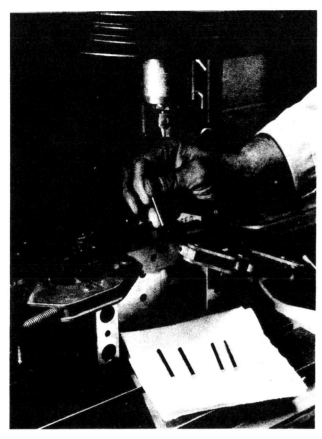

Fig. 4-20   Gage pins can be used in a jig grinder to check small hole sizes without disturbing the machine set-up.

accuracy (XXXX to Z) and in all sizes and sets ranging in .0001 in., or larger increments, depending upon the application. This enables the operator to work within .0001 in. tolerance when required (refer to Fig. 4-20). A dial bore gage is frequently used to further check for roundness and straightness. Gage pins are a part of the plug gage family. (Refer to screened note on previous page.)

END MEASURING RODS

End measuring rods are made of hardened tool steel and have ends ground to a spherical radius to ensure single point contact with the surfaces being measured. Some have grips made of rubber or other insulating material to help avoid thermal expansion from the heat of the user's hands.

End measuring rods are usually available in increments of one inch or 25mm, and are useful for setting micrometers and other instruments,

and for setting or checking table stops on machine tools such as jig borers, where table locations must be very accurate. Some end measuring rods are especially designed for setting machine tools and are made with a raised collar to fit grooves in the machine table. These types of end measuring rods may also be used with a special micrometer head to allow measurement to the nearest .0001″ between the incremental sizes of the rods themselves.

End measuring rods are also useful for checking parallel surfaces and large ring diameters where a solid plug gage would be too heavy to be practical. They are readily available in lengths up to about two feet and longer ones can be made by gage suppliers on special order.

LENGTH GAGES

A length gage is a special device designed to replace a rule for measuring distances. This type of gage is used when a large number of parts is to be made, because it allows the workpieces to be checked quickly.

SCREW THREAD GAGES

The types of threads commonly used in industry include the American National, the British Standard Whitworth, the Unified, the American National Acme, the Worm, the Square, and the International Metric. The Unified thread is predominant in this country. Classes of threads are

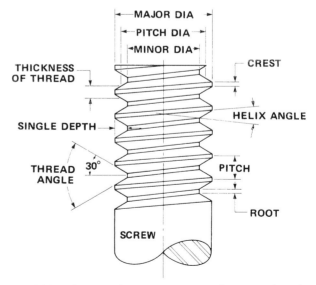

Fig. 4-21   Commonly measured parts of a screw thread.

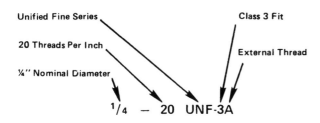

Fig. 4-22 Typical designation of a thread.

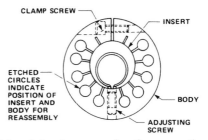

Fig. 4-24 Adjusting screw for the screw thread ring gage.

identified by number and letter (1A, 2A, 2B, 3B, etc.). The number indicates the fit in terms of tolerance and allowance while the designation "A" applies to external threads and "B" applies to internal threads. Figure 4-21 illustrates the commonly measured parts of a screw thread. Figure 4-22 illustrates the typical designation of a thread.

Screw thread GO and NOT-GO gages (see Fig. 4-23) are similar to the ring and plug gages described previously, with the exception that thread ring gages are usually capable of being adjusted. These gages are primarily used for checking the pitch diameter of internal or external screw threads.

To avoid damaging threaded parts or the gages themselves, these gages must only be used by hand. They should never be mated or tightened to a part with clamps or wrenches. Screw thread gages must be recertified periodically to a master thread gage. In general practice, a NOT-GO condition is acceptable if the gage enters not more than one turn (or thread) with the part being inspected.

The NOT-GO thread ring gage checks only the pitch diameter to insure that it is not below the minimum tolerance. The GO thread ring gage checks the maximum pitch diameter, and verifies adequate clearance at the minor diameter, flank angle and lead.

The NOT-GO thread plug gage checks only the pitch diameter to insure that it is not above the maximum limit. The GO thread plug gage checks the minimum pitch diameter, and verifies clearance at the major diameter, flank angle and the lead.

If the plug enters the internal thread completely and the NOT-GO condition has been verified, assembly with the mating external thread is guaranteed.

Inspection of the major and minor diameter on external threads is done with snap gages. The minor diameter on internal threads uses a simple cylindrical plug gage. To check the major diameter on internal threads, the flanks of the thread plug gage are reduced to allow for minimal interference. (See Fig. 6-28 and 6-29.)

Most standard screw thread ring gages contain some device for adjusting and locking the gage. The unique four-piece construction thread ring gage, shown in Fig. 4-23, contains two screws, one for size adjustment and a second for exerting uniform clamping pressure on the threaded insert. As shown in Fig. 4-24, the adjusting screw contacts a coined area on the insert, and—because of an elliptical head—shifts the threads on the insert along the helix angle when takeup is made to compensate for wear. This screw is advanced to enlarge, and backed off to decrease, the thread ring gage size.

The taperlock, reversible, and annular designs adopted for screw thread plug gages are similar to those used for plain cylindrical plug gages, except the length of the thread gaging members differs in some instances. The taperlock type of gage (see Fig. 4-25) is also used for pipe thread gages ranging from $1/16$ to 2 in. nominal pipe sizes, whereas the reversible design is used for $2^1/2$ to 6 in. nominal pipe sizes.

Fig. 4-23 Screw thread ring gages. (Courtesy of DoAll Company)

Fig. 4-25 Taperlock screw thread plug gage. (Courtesy of DoAll Company)

CHAPTER IV REVIEW

1. Explain why knife-edge straightedges have a semicircular cross-section at the test edge.

2. True or False: A wire gage measures wire diameters with its circular holes and sheet metal thickness between its slots.

3. Explain why accuracy of the small hole gage depends heavily upon the skill of the person using it.

4. How accurate should a gage generally be in terms of the tolerance of the parts it is to test?

5. What would be the sizes of a pair of GO/NOT—GO gages made to check a diameter of $1.000^{+.005}_{-.003}$? What would the tolerances on the gages themselves be likely to be?

6. Name the various gages needed to check a screw thread completely.

7. Match the appropriate gage to the measurement checks listed below:

    A.   To check a 6″ hole diameter   a)   Center gage

    B.   Width of a slot (about .025″)   b)   Small hole gage

    C.   Grinding a form tool to a $^7/_{64}$″ radius   c)   Feeler gage

    D.   Grinding a threading tool to cut a 60° sharp-V thread   d)   End measuring rod

    E.   Width of a slot (about .250″)   e)   Radius gage

8. Explain how "Maximum Material Condition" and "Least Material Condition" relate to mating parts.

9. What are the four types of plug gages?

10. What are the three basic designs of plain ring gages?

Chapter V

Surface Plates, Accessories, and Gages

In-work and finished parts are frequently inspected on a surface plate, using a variety of gages and measuring equipment. This chapter will cover the types of surface plates and hand-manipulated tools, while indicating and mechanical comparator equipment are covered in the following chapter.

SURFACE PLATES

Surface plates provide a true, smooth, plane surface made from granite, semisteel, or cast iron that has been carefully machined, lapped or hand-scraped. They are sometimes equipped with threaded inserts to secure workpieces and/or surface plate accessories. A variety of inspection setups are made on surface plates with height gages, gage blocks, dial test indicators, sine bars and plates, cylindrical squares, parallel bars, V-blocks, angle plates, and clamps for measuring linear and angular

dimensions, as well as gaging dimensions of limit, form, and position. Simple or complex workpieces can be measured for length, thickness, flatness, parallelism, location, straightness, squareness, angle, hole location, profile, or other features on surface plates.

The granite surface plate is most commonly used today. Cast iron and semisteel plates are less durable, harder to maintain and thus are less economical.

To test a part surface for flatness on a surface plate, first carefully clean the part, and remove all burrs. Then place that surface on the surface plate, as shown in Fig. 5-1. Any rocking motion that is apparent indicates a variance in flatness of the piece being tested.

Cast Iron and Semisteel Surface Plates

Cast iron and semisteel surface plates are made from high quality castings that have been aged to relieve internal stresses and reduce distortion in the final working surface. Both kinds of plates are heavily ribbed and reinforced on their undersides for stability. Cast plates vary in size from small bench plates that are a few inches square, to sizes as large or larger than 4 by 8 ft. The large cast plates are usually 12 in. or more thick, and are generally mounted on a heavy supporting stand or legs. Any plate must be leveled periodically to insure that its working surface remains perfectly flat. The cast plates must be kept as dry as possible to prevent their surfaces from corroding.

Fig. 5-1   *Testing a surface for flatness on a cast iron surface plate.*

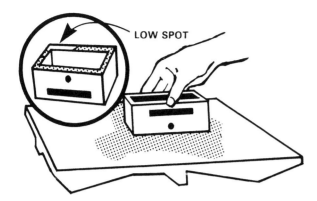

Fig. 5-2A   Using Prussian blue to aid in testing a flat surface on a cast iron surface plate.

Since the metal plates are fairly soft, care must be taken not to damage the surface. A surface plate should *never* be used as an anvil, nor as a base for hammering which could damage the surface or cause distortion and destroy the integrity of the surface flatness.

An old method for checking flatness is to first lightly coat a cast iron surface plate with Prussian blue (bearing blue), and then slide the piece being tested across the blue surface, as shown in Fig. 5-2A. The low spots on the surface being tested will not take the blue; the high spots will (see insert Fig. 5-2A). Note: Blueing should not be used on a granite surface plate.

To determine how much variation there is from flatness—and where it is—you can insert a blade or blades of a thickness gage, as shown in Fig. 5-3. Remember to add the thickness of all of the blades together to obtain the total variation.

A faster, more modern, and more accurate method of checking squareness is a master squareness gage with dial test indicator used on a granite surface plate such as the one shown in Fig. 3-11 and Fig. 5-2B. Such gages should be used when accuracy must be closer than ±.001 in.

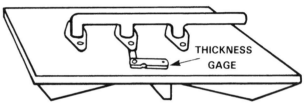

Fig. 5-3   Measuring the conformity of a flat surface using a thickness gage.

Granite Surface Plates

Granite surface plates are considered to be superior to the cast iron and semisteel surface plates because granite is harder, denser, and waterproof. Granite is a natural material that has aged in the Earth for a very long time. Therefore, it has little internal stress.

Granite surface plates range in size from about 12 by 18 in. to 4 by 12 ft. A large granite plate can be anywhere from 10 to 20 in. thick, and weigh as much as 5 to 10 tons. Some granite plates are finished on both sides, thereby extending their useful life by allowing them to be turned over.

Fig. 5-6A, B and C are examples of the use of accessories on a granite surface plate. You can lay the work to be tested directly on the plate, clamp it to angle plates, or hold it on V-blocks.

Granite plates are available in three grades, as shown in Fig. 5-4. The tolerances given are unilateral, referenced to the distance between two parallel planes, the base plane and the roof plane.

Fig. 5-2B   A vertical squareness gage is a fast, highly accurate surface plate accessory for checking squareness. (Courtesy of PMC Industries.)

Care of Surface Plates

Surface plates are very expensive. Therefore, take care to protect them from damage. Make sure that all parts laid out on a surface plate are clean and free from burrs. You can remove burrs by stoning or filing them. In addition:

(1) Do not allow anything to drop on the surface plate.
(2) Place only those items that you need on the plate. Never lay heavy tools on its surface.
(3) Do not perform any hammering or punching operations while the work is on the plate.

(4) When a cast iron or steel plate is not in use, apply a light film of oil to its surface to prevent rust.
(5) Cover the surface of both metal and granite plates with a heavy felt pad followed by a sheet metal or wood cover to prevent accidental damage to the plate.
(6) Wipe the surface plate periodically with a cleaning solution prepared specifically for surface plates. The solution helps prevent abrasion by dirt particles and also acts to remove grease. Even on granite surface plates water should not be used since it could cause rust on precision tools.

Figure 5-4: Total Flatness Tolerance of Granite Surface Plates in Microinches.

Rectangular Plates		Grade AA	Grade A	Grade B
Width	Length Inches			
12	12	50	100	200
12	18	50	100	200
18	18	50	100	200
18	24	75	150	300
24	24	75	150	300
24	36	100	200	400
24	48	150	300	600
36	36	150	300	600
36	48	200	400	800
36	60	250	500	1000
36	72	300	600	1200
48	48	200	400	800
48	60	300	600	1200
48	72	350	700	1400
48	96	500	1000	2000
48	120	700	1400	2800
60	120	750	1500	3000
72	96	600	1200	2400
72	144	1100	2200	4400
Round Plates Diameter				
12		50	100	200
18		50	100	200
24		775	150	300
36		100	200	400
48		125	250	500

BENCH PLATES

Bench plates are small surface plates machined to a very smooth flat surface, usually from cast iron. Bench plates vary in size. An average-sized bench plate is about 18 in. square, and about 1$\frac{1}{2}$ in. thick. You use the bench plate on a bench as a base upon which to work. Setups that require hammering or peening should be done on bench plates and not on granite surface plates.

Such smaller iron plates are vulnerable to many sources of error and should not be relied upon for close tolerance work. Small granite plates are more accurate, but are heavier and therefore, less portable.

SURFACE GAGES

Surfaces gages with dial test indicators are used in conjunction with surface plates to measure height, check the parallelism and flatness of a plane surface, and with a scriber attachment to scribe layout lines on vertical surfaces. They consist of a base with an adjustable spindle (see Fig. 5-5 & 6-34) to which a scriber or a dial test indicator may be clamped. Surface gages are made in several sizes, classified by the height of their spindles. Spindles range in height from 4 to 18 in., the average being 9 or 12 in. high. The bottom of some surface gages has a deep V-groove cut into it, which allows the gage to be set on a cylindrical surface.

The spindle of a universal surface gage can be adjusted to any angle with respect to the base, and tightened in place with the spindle nut. The rocker adjusting screw provides for the fine adjustment

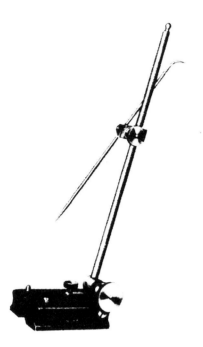

Fig. 5-5   Universal surface gage with scriber. (Courtesy of Brown & Sharpe Manufacturing Company)

of the spindle by pivoting the spindle rocker bracket. The scriber can be positioned at any height and in any desired direction on the spindle by tightening the nut on the swivel bolt. You can also replace the spindle with the scriber, and use it in situations where the working space is limited, and the height of the work is within range of the scriber.

To use a surface gage for scribing layout lines, first wipe off the top of a surface plate and the bottom of the surface gage. Place the surface gage on the surface plate making sure that the gage is resting squarely on the flat plate. The scriber point can now be adjusted to the desired height by using the adjustment screws on the surface gage. For work that only requires accuracy to about $\pm^1/_{64}$, a rule and rule holder or a combination square can be used to adjust the surface gage to the desired size. Simply wipe off the bottom of the rule holder or square and place it squarely on the surface plate and make the required adjustment. The part to be layed out can now be wiped, rested on the plate and lines scribed to their proper dimension by carefully sliding the surface gage on the surface plate. (See Fig. 2-12B.)

A

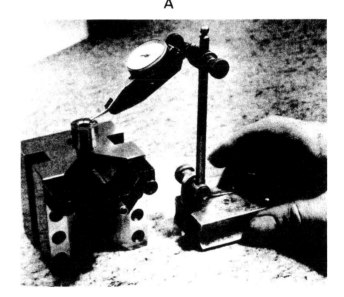

B

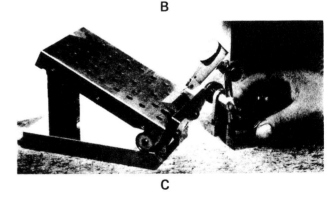

C

Fig. 5-6   Some applications of the versatile surface gage on a granite plate (A) with dial test indicator - using gage blocks to transfer the height setting; (B) checking the end of a bushing for flatness or squareness with the part held upright in a V-block; and (C) checking the angularity and flatness of a precision part using a sine plate and gage blocks.

For more accurate work, the surface gage with the dial test indicator must be set to a more accurate standard, such as a stack of precision gage blocks (covered later in this chapter). Surface gages used with dial test indicators (see Fig. 5-6A) will provide a direct reading of the amount of difference between the surface being inspected and the desired dimension. The indicator may be clamped directly to the surface gage spindle. The indicator probe is set to the desired height using gage blocks. Adjust the indicator to zero using the rocker adjustment screw found at the back of the base of most surface gages. Once set, the surface gage must be handled carefully to avoid accidentally changing the adjustment.

Another use of a surface gage with a dial test indicator is to check the trueness of cylindrical surfaces. You first place the shaft in a V-block, set the gage in position, and then turn the shaft slowly. If the shaft is not true, the dial hand will indicate the deviation. When used with a dial test indicator the surface gage can be used to provide a direct indicator reading of "runout," and to check flatness, squareness and other dimensional features.

The surface gage is a precision instrument and requires periodic maintenance. The surface gage base (datum) must be checked periodically for flatness and the rocker arm adjusted to eliminate play. When you are not using the surface gage, store it carefully in a safe place to avoid damaging it.

HEIGHT GAGES

Another measuring instrument that is used in conjunction with a surface plate is the height gage. Height gages are used to measure vertical distances. Several different types are available, including vernier and micrometer.

Vernier Height Gage

An application of the vernier scale to a height gage is shown in Fig. 5-7. This instrument is similar

in principle to the vernier caliper, except that it rests on a heavy base and has a beveled pointer on the movable jaw. The graduated bar is held in a vertical position by a finely-ground and lapped base.

Vernier height gages are available in sizes ranging from 6 to 72 in. All current models have

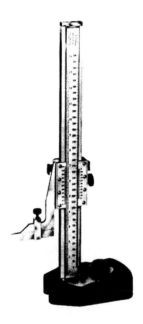

Fig. 5-7 Dual inch-millimeter vernier height gage. (Courtesy of The L. S. Starrett Company)

fine-adjustment provision and a scriber attachment that permits scribing a workpiece to 0.001 in. accuracy with the gage, itself. Some models have a quick-adjusting screw release on the movable jaw that allows you to move directly to the approximate desired reading within the range, and then to zero-in using the fine-adjustment mechanism. The accuracy of these gages can be checked in many ways. Perhaps the simplest method—and the one most widely used—is to check with stacks of gage blocks from an accurate surface plate.

In using this instrument, place the work on a surface plate, and measure all distances from this reference elevation. The reading of the 25- or 50-division adjustable vernier plate is identical to that of a vernier caliper.

Fig. 5-8   Metric height gage with micrometer head and digital readout. (Courtesy of Brown & Sharpe Manufacturing Company)

Micrometer Height Gage

A precision metric height gage with a micrometer head and a digital readout is shown in Fig. 5-8. Height settings are obtained by combining the accuracy of gage blocks with the precision readings of the micrometer head. The micrometer height gage basically consists of two major parts: (1) the measuring column of stacked and permanently-wrung 10mm gage blocks, and (2) the micrometer head with 500 equal divisions on its thimble.

The gage block column moves up and down over a 10mm range by operation of the micrometer head. Scales on the left side of the gage blocks read to the nearest 10mm, the digital readout gives the 0.01mm reading, and the final 0.001mm is read directly from the micrometer head. Both over and under heights can be checked directly from the gage blocks in a single setting, because reference surfaces are provided on both the top and bottom of each block; the top and bottom of adjacent blocks are in exactly the same plane. Therefore, the need to add or subtract block thickness is eliminated.

One complete revolution of the micrometer head moves the measuring column 0.5mm. Because the head has 500 equal divisions on its thimble,

each of the smallest divisions of the thimble represents 0.001mm or 1 micrometer.

The digital counter eliminates possible reading errors, and permits fast height transfer operations. The first digit on the counter is in millimeters; the second is in tenths of a millimeter; and the last is in hundredths of a millimeter. The larger dimensions (exceeding 9.99 millimeters) are relayed to the vertical scale marked by the measuring column. Inch-based micrometer height gages are also available, and are used in the same manner to obtain accurate measurements in increments of .0001″.

PRECISION GAGE BLOCKS

Although precision gage blocks are end standards (see Chapter I), they are also used in the shop to directly check parts in all stages of manufacture. Used with and without accessories, the blocks can check length, inside or outside measurements, locations, plug or production gages, height gages, micrometers, etc. (see Fig. 5-9). They are also used to set mechanical, electrical, and electronic gages, and make up into super-accurate height and snap gages. (Recall that, in Chapter III, you learned that precision angle gage blocks are used to construct and check angles.)

The U. S. Federal Specifications recognize four grades of gage blocks, as shown in Fig. 5-10 and 5-13, of which three are used in industry. The

Fig. 5-9   Typical gage block set being used to check a micrometer. (Courtesy of Brown & Sharpe Manufacturing Company)

precise Laboratory Grade 1 (formerly Class AA) is used for experimental work and research, and are sometimes called *master gage blocks*. The Inspection Grade 2 (formerly Class A+) is used for checking gages in the toolroom and for inspection of finished part dimensions. The Work Grade 3 (a compromise between former Classes A and B) blocks are the ones that are assembled into actual working gages for accurate dimensional measuring in the shop.

Precision gage blocks are manufactured in sets consisting of from 5 to over 100 blocks. This allows a systematic progression of measurements to be obtained by combining blocks. Gage block sets are commonly available that permit combinations in increments of 25 millionths of an inch (0.000025 in.), as shown in Fig. 5-14.

Gage blocks are square or rectangular blocks (see Fig. 5-11) made from steel, chrome-plated steel, or solid chromium or tungsten carbides that have been lapped to a particular size. Individual blocks have two surfaces that are flat and parallel. The parallel distance between the surfaces is the size engraved on the block to a guaranteed tolerance as

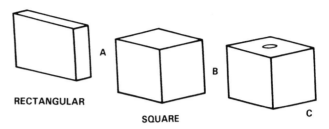

RECTANGULAR   SQUARE   SQUARE, WITH CENTER HOLE

Fig. 5-11 Styles of gage blocks: (A) rectangular, (B) square without center hole, and (C) square with center accessory hole.

given in Fig. 5-10 and 5-13 at an ambient temperature of 68°F. When wrung firmly together, stacks of gage blocks form a new end standard equal to the sum of the sizes of the individual blocks. For example, with a set of 81 blocks, any length expressed in four decimal places from 0.2000 in. to approximately 12.0000 in., can be built up. Between 0.3000 in. and 4.0000 in., three to four gage groups can be built at the same time from a set to an identical length expressed in four decimal places.

Figure 5-10: Tolerances on Length of Gage Blocks, Inch System, at the Reference Point.*

Nominal Size	0.5 (Formerly Grade AAA)		1 (Formerly Grade AA)		2 (Formerly Grade A+)		3 (Compromise between Former Grades A and B)	
	Plus	Minus	Plus	Minus	Plus	Minus	Plus	Minus
Inches	Tolerances in Microinches							
1 or less	1	1	2	2	4	2	8	4
2	2	2	4	4	8	4	16	8
3	3	3	5	5	10	5	20	10
4	4	4	6	6	12	6	24	12
Long Gage Blocks 5			7	7	14	7	28	14
6			8	8	16	8	32	16
7			9	9	18	9	36	18
8			10	10	20	10	40	20
10			12	12	24	12	48	24
12			14	14	28	14	56	28
16			18	18	36	18	72	36
20			20	20	40	20	80	40

* From Federal Specification GGG-G-15C, 1975.

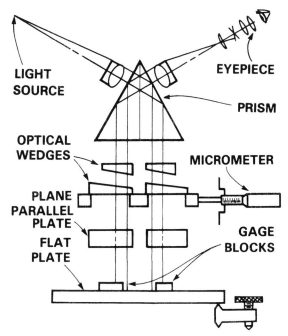

LIGHT SOURCE

EYEPIECE

PRISM

OPTICAL WEDGES

MICROMETER

PLANE PARALLEL PLATE

FLAT PLATE

GAGE BLOCKS

Fig. 5-12   Interferometric comparator comparing one gage block with another.

Gage blocks are calibrated by interferometry as shown in Fig. 5-12. Their actual sizes are determined by comparison with the wavelength of red light in the color spectrum in accordance with the international standard of length. Thus, gage blocks translate this international standard into a practical form for use in the shop.

Each set of gage blocks is supplied with a fitted hardwood case, which keeps the blocks neatly arranged for easy selection, as well as protecting them from dirt, oil, and damage. The case usually has extra compartments for two wear blocks that are 0.050 or 0.100 in. thick. Wear blocks are generally provided with any basic set.

When you use gage blocks you must select the exact combination of blocks to give you the dimension required. Usually, you start by selecting from the larger blocks, and then add smaller ones to obtain the dimension, using as few blocks as you can. Once you have selected a stack of blocks, you must then stack them properly. Much of their

Nominal Size	Tolerance Grade							
	0.5 (Formerly Grade AAA)		1 (Formerly Grade AA)		2 (Formerly Grade A+)		3 (Compromise between Former Grades A and B)	
	Plus	Minus	Plus	Minus	Plus	Minus	Plus	Minus
Millimeters	Tolerances in Micrometers							
10 or less	0.03	0.03	0.05	0.05	0.10	0.05	0.20	0.10
Over 10 thru 25	.04	.04	.08	.08	.15	.08	.30	.15
Over 25 thru 50	.05	.05	.10	.10	.20	.10	.40	.20
Over 50 thru 75	.06	.06	.13	.13	.25	.12	.45	.22
Over 75 thru 100	.08	.08	.15	.15	.30	.15	.60	.30
Long Gage Blocks 125			.18	.18	.35	.18	.70	.35
150			.20	.20	.40	.20	.80	.40
175			.23	.23	.45	.22	.90	.45
200			.25	.25	.50	.25	1.00	.50
250			.30	.30	.60	.30	1.20	.60
300			.35	.35	.70	.35	1.40	.70
400			.45	.45	.90	.45	1.80	.90
500			.50	.50	1.00	.50	2.00	1.00

* From Federal Specification GGG-G-15C, 1975.

Fig. 5-13   Tolerances on Length of Gage Blocks, Metric System, at the Reference Point. *

Pieces in the Set	Number of Blocks per Series	Size Range (Inch)	Series Increment (Inch)
15	4	.0501 to .0503 plus .0506	.0001
	4	.051 to .053 plus .056	.001
	4	.010 to .030 plus .060	.010
	4	.100 to .300 plus .600	.100
	3	1.000 to 3.000	1.000
35	9	.1001 to .1009	.0001
	9	.101 to .109	.001
	9	.110 to .190	.010
	5	.100 to .500	.100
	3	1.000 to 3.000	1.000
81	9	.1001 to .1009	.0001
	50	.101 to .150	.001
	18	.050 to .950	.050
	4	1.000 to 4.000	1.000
84	3	Same as the 81-piece set, with addition of 0.100025 to 0.100075	.000025

* The individual blocks contained in the sets are listed in series.

Fig. 5-14   Typical Gage Block Sets.*

precision depends upon the way they are stacked. The correct method of joining them together is called "wringing," as shown in Fig. 5-15. A wear block is used at each end of the stack.

Be sure that the gage blocks are absolutely free of any foreign matter when you use them. Also, be sure that your hands are clean and free from oil or dirt. Grease-soiled hands are rarely free from grit, and grit is harmful to gage blocks. Avoid touching the gaging surfaces of the blocks with your hands as much as possible. Perspiration on your hands contains an acid that causes corrosion. Keep all surfaces and parts that come into contact with the gage block gaging surfaces clean.

The proper method for "wringing" the blocks is: Two clean cloth pads should be used—one pad to be moistened with only a few drops of a silicone base oil such as Dow Corning FS-1265 Fluid 1000

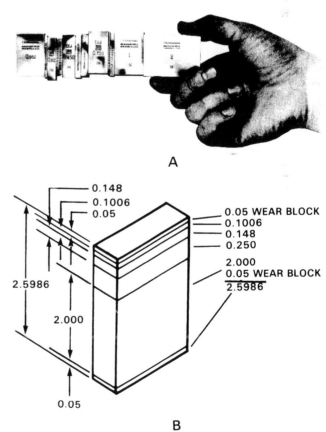

A

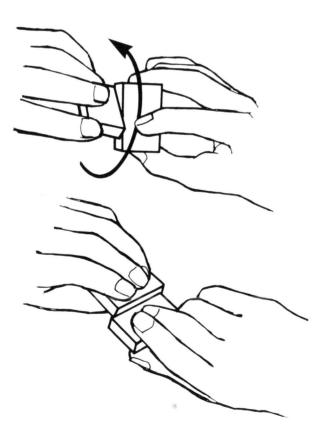

Fig. 5-15   Wringing gage blocks together.

Fig. 5-16   Stack of gage and wear blocks wrung together. (Courtesy of Brown & Sharpe Manufacturing Company)

Centistrokes, the other a dry pad. A good grade of linen, two or three layers thick, over a board 4" x 6" is sufficient. Upon wiping the block with a clean towel, the two gaging surfaces to be "wrung" are wiped across the slightly moistened silicone oil pad and then across the dry pad. Slide the gage surfaces together and align the edges. If after "wringing" the gages slide too easily, they have not been wiped sufficiently on the dry pad. If the surfaces refuse to "wring," they have been wiped too dry and the procedure must be repeated. Properly wrung stacks of gage blocks will adhere to each other enough to defy the force of gravity (see Fig. 5-16A).

Gage blocks have many uses in the machine shop. One of the primary uses is to check other gaging devices. For example, you can use them as standards to check the accuracy of such instruments as a micrometer, vernier caliper, and height gage. You can also use them as the standard for setting comparison instruments and sine bars.

TOOLMAKER'S FLATS

Toolmaker's flats (see Fig. 5-17) are disks made from steel or granite that are ground and lapped to a high degree of flatness, comparable to the surface of a gage block. In inspection, toolmaker's flats serve as a mounting surface for gage block assemblies and similar high-precision instruments used in dimensional measurements. Toolmaker's flats range in size from 6 to 48 in. in diameter, 2 to 16 in. in thickness, and to 10 millionths of an inch in accuracy.

SURFACE PLATE ACCESSORIES

Common accessories used with surface plates include parallel bars, V-blocks, sine bars, sine plates, plain right angle plates, universal right angle plates, and the toolmaker's vise and clamp. Surface plate accessories may be made from iron, semisteel, or granite.

Parallel Bars

Parallel bars (sometimes called *parallel blocks* or *solid parallels*) are rectangular pieces of steel, cast iron, or granite that are machined so that

Fig. 5-17   Toolmaker's flat. (Courtesy of DoAll Company)

their opposite surfaces are parallel to each other (see Fig. 5-18). As shown, they are generally used in matched pairs. The adjacent surfaces of parallel bars are at right angles to each other in contrast to adjustable parallels (see Chapter III) whose adjacent surfaces are set at other angles. Parallel bars are used when projections on the workpiece prevent setting it directly on the surface plate, or when you want to raise workpieces above the surface plate and still maintain parallelism. They are also used to back workpieces on milling machines, shapers, and drilling tables.

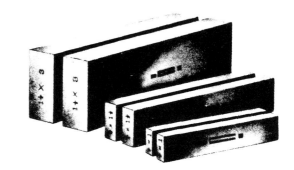

Fig. 5-18   Parallel bars. (Courtesy of Brown & Sharpe Manufacturing Company)

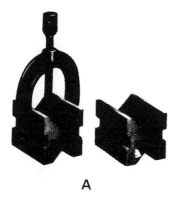

A

V-Blocks

V-Blocks are used to hold round stock on surface plates and to prevent it from rolling or moving around. They have a 90 deg V-shaped slot cut into the top and bottom, usually of different depths as shown in Fig. 5-19. You place the stock in the appropriate slot lengthwise, and secure it with a clamp if necessary.

Sine Bars and Sine Plates

Sine bars and sine plates can be used to measure or construct very accurate angles, as you learned in Chapter III. Gage blocks are used to construct the elevation for the "side opposite" (see Fig. 5-20).

B

*Fig. 5-19   A) V-block with and without clamp.
B) Checking the end of a bushing with the part held upright in a V-block.*

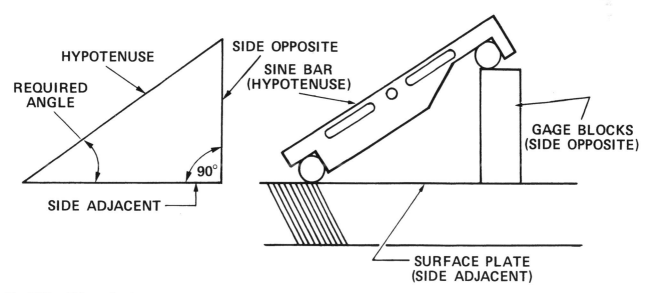

Fig. 5-20   Using a sine bar.

A   B

Fig. 5-21   A) Plain right angle plates made of iron; B) Indicating a part straight that is clamped to an angle plate for surface grinding.

Plain Right Angle Plates

Plain right angle plates (see Fig. 5-21A) have accurately machined surfaces at right angles to each other are used on surface plates in conjunction with a surface gage and dial indicator (refer to 5-21B) to check perpendicularity. In use, you mount the workpiece at right angles to the surface plate by clamping it against the right angle plate.

Universal Right Angle Plates

Universal right angle plates (see Fig. 5-22) are used in applications similar to plain right angle

plates, except that they offer six surfaces that are square and parallel.

Toolmaker's Vise and Clamps

A toolmaker's vise (see Fig. 5-23A) is used for inspection and to drill, fit, and lay out work on surface plates. The V-groove in the base takes work from $9/32$ to $11/16$ in. in diameter. The tongue on the large jaw slides in the groove, and is held in place by a strap that prevents the jaw from lifting. The jaws have a $1^{15}/16$ in. capacity.

The toolmaker's clamp (see Fig. 5-23B) is used to clamp work onto the edge of a surface plate or to right angle plates (see above). The ends of the

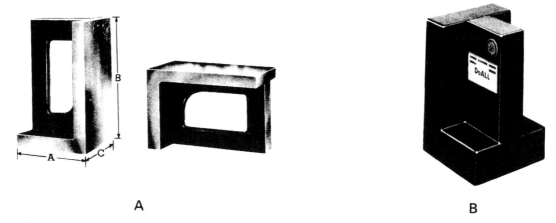

A   B

Fig. 5-22   Universal right angle plates: iron (A) and black granite (B). (Courtesy of DoAll Company)

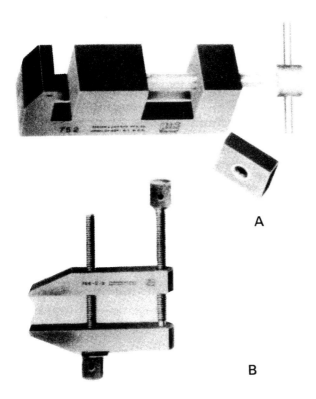

A

B

*Fig. 5-23   Toolmaker's vise and clamp. (Courtesy of
Brown & Sharpe Manufacturing Company)*

jaws are chamfered to facilitate clamping a workpiece under a shoulder or in a recess. A clip holds
the loose jaw in position when the clampscrew is
released. The jaws have a capacity ranging from
$5/8$ to $3^{1}/_{2}$ in. (16 to 89mm).

CHAPTER V REVIEW

1. Using the sets of gage blocks referenced in Fig. 5-14, select the gage blocks needed to wring stacks to the following dimensions, using the fewest blocks needed. Assume that there are two extra blocks of .050 in each set for use as wear blocks.

    Example: Using the 15-block set, wring a stack to 3.2066";

    Solution:

.050	wear block
.0506	
.056	
3.000	
+ .050	wear block
3.2066"	

    Using the 15 pc. set in Fig. 5-14 plus two .050" wear blocks, select combinations to make the following stacks:

    a) 4.14141   b) 3.3333   c)   1.6009

    Using the 35 pc. set and two .050" wear blocks, find:

    d) 4.0625   e) 1.9875   f)   2.5400

    Using the 81 pc. set and two .050" wear blocks, find:

    g) .457   h) 1.9887   i)   7.3865

    Using the 84 pc. set and two .050" wear blocks, find:

    j)   11.000000   k) .987650   l) 2.556225

2. Determine the gage block stacks necessary for sine-bar elevations to generate the following angles, using the 81-piece set referenced in Fig. 5-14:

    With a 5" sine bar: a) 62°   b) 35° 30'   c) 29° 14'   d) 10° 10'50"

    With a 10" sine bar: e) 46° 25'30"   f) 21° 19'20"   g) 60° 50'45"   h) 50° 31'22"

3. Using the 81-piece set referenced in figure 5-14, select gage blocks to produce the following sine-bar elevations. Also, find the angles.

    With a 5" sine bar:

    a) 5.1414   b) 3.3530   c) 2.1574   d) 4.0000   e) 6.5000

    With a 10" sine bar:

    f) 3.2511   g) 5.1414   h) 2.0000   i) 7.1267   j) 5.9355

4. Be able to demonstrate to the satisfaction of your instructor or supervisor the proper method of handling and wringing gage blocks, the use and care of surface plates, and the use, selection and care of surface plate accessories.

Chapter VI

Mechanical Comparators and Indicating Gages

In contrast to fixed-size and limit gages that only determine whether or not a product is within tolerance limits, sometimes you need an instrument or gage that will measure *how much* a part deviates from specifications. Such an instrument is called an *adjustable gage* or, commonly, a *comparator*.

INTRODUCTION TO COMPARATORS

Adjustable gages indicate the amount by which a measured part deviates, plus or minus, from a standard to which the gage has been set. In most cases, the deviation is indicated directly in units of measurement but, in some cases, the gages indicate only whether the deviation is within a particular range. Nearly all comparators amplify the input signal from the sensor so that very small deviations can be detected. These gages are adjustable, which makes them useful in gaging a wide range of sizes. They are relatively easy and rapid to use, which makes them suitable for production gaging.

A comparator consists of several joined functional elements that: (1) sense and discriminate the dimension to be measured from all other conditions, (2) compare the magnitude of the dimension to a reference magnitude, (3) produce a corresponding mechanical motion, pneumatic pressure, or electrical signal, (4) transmit the motion, pressure, or signal by means of linkage, tubing, or wiring, and (5) express the results by

deflecting a pointer or actuating a counter to display the information on an indicator.

Indicators

Indicators are display devices that are classified as either analog or digital. Analog displays provide a continually varying response; for example, a pointer on a scale, an ink line on a chart, or a light trace on a cathode-ray tube. Digital displays always provide numerical information. Typical examples include digital counters, and typed or printed log sheets. When using analog display devices, you can tell at a glance the approximate value as well as the relative value of a dimension with respect to the full scale. However, you cannot read analog devices as quickly and accurately as digital devices. The numerical or digital display can be as precise as desired, limited only by the number of digits contained in the display and the accuracy of the signal source. The measurement unit for the variable being measured can also be displayed along with the value.

The most common visual display mechanism is the pointer moving in relation to a graduated scale, usually marked to read directly in measurement units.

An important cause of pointer-reading error is the parallax (or apparent difference in position) when the pointer and the scale are not in the same plane. Parallax can be reduced by providing a mirror sector in the plane of the scale, or by using a pointer shaped like a thin vane rather than a needle. A thin vane aligns the eye of the observer, the pointer, and the mirror image of the pointer for reading, and improves consistency of readings.

TYPES OF COMPARATORS

Two classes of comparator are in common use in the shop, one in which the comparison is made pneumatically or optically, the other in which comparison is made by contact. To check a gaged part, a comparator is usually preset to the basic critical dimension to be inspected (for example, to 1.505 in the dimension 1.505±0.005, or 2.000 in 2.000±0.002) with a master having that dimension, or by two masters: one for the maximum limit and one for minimum limit. A general-purpose comparator can also be set with gage blocks.

Contact Comparators

The two basic types of contact comparators are mechanical and electrical. All contact comparators are similar in their physical arrangement, differing only in their method of amplifying and indicating the deviation from the master setting.

A general-purpose contact comparator usually consists of: (1) a contact point, points, or surface, (2) a sensor, and (3) a means for physically maintaining the distance between (1) and (2). This means often takes the form of a C-frame in a gage making external measurements, or the form of a plug in a gage making internal measurements. The indicator or meter that displays the results, may be either an integral part of the measuring head or a separate unit.

The sensor or comparator head amplifies the linear movement of the contact point enough so that tiny movements are made clearly visible on a remote indicator. Comparator heads are frequently rated by the amount of their magnification. Thus, a 1000:1 comparator would have a 1 in. travel of the indicating hand or pointer or marker for each 0.001 in. movement of the contact point. Movement in mechanical comparators is usually magnified by a rack, pinion, and pointer, or by a parallelogram arrangement. In general, mechanical comparators can be applied to tolerances of 0.0001 in.

Movement in electrical comparators is amplifed by several methods, the most popular being a trans-

former or a floating core in a solenoid attached to the contact point. Linear movement of the contact changes the penetration of the core into the field of the solenoid coil. The resulting change in coil reactance is amplified electrically. Electrical comparators are applied to tolerances in the range of 0.00005 to 0.001 in., although the accuracy of the instrument itself may be as fine as 0.000001 in.

Contact comparators are used to check both individual single measurements or groups of single measurements. Their accuracy depends on the comparator head. In addition, several contact comparators can be assembled as a single gaging device to perform multiple measurements. Sometimes all dimensions on a part are inspected simultaneously on one machine. When the amplifying heads in such a machine are arranged to actuate sorting equipment and to separate within-tolerance from out-of-tolerance parts, inspection is said to be automated.

Pneumatic Comparators

Intermediate in operation between contact and optical comparators are the pneumatic types, which sense the distance between the surface of a part and the contact by means of an air-stream. This comparator brings a precision orifice so close to the surface to be measured that the flow of air from the orifice is restricted. The closer the orifice comes to the surface, the greater the restriction. Measuring the restriction in flow gives, in effect, a measurement of the distance that the orifice is from the surface. The accuracy range of pneumatic comparators is approximately that of electric comparators.

Optical Comparators

General-purpose visual or optical comparators differ physically from the other types of comparators. They consist of: (1) a light source, (2) a staging area on which to place the part being inspected, (3) a series of lenses and mirrors for magnifying and projecting the shadow of the object, and (4) a viewing screen on which the image is projected, usually made from frosted glass.

Optical or visual comparators are generally used to inspect complex forms, or the relationship between one or more individual surfaces. The image of the part being checked is projected on the screen and this image is compared and measured to a standard "X-Y" radius chart or, in the case of specific complex forms, with a custom designed chart which details the location of a surface or contour. The accuracy of optical comparators is influenced by the quality of the optical system employed, the type of light source and the reflectiveness of the surface being checked. High precision parts are usually highly finished and have a more reflective surface. This reflection creates an aberration (or fuzziness) on the screen that makes it difficult to identify the actual surface image. Modern comparators with precision optics and/or a mercury arc light source which permits higher magnification, provide accuracy to ±0.0002 in. while older machines were generally limited to accuracy of ±0.001 in.

MECHANICAL CONTACT COMPARATORS

Mechanical contact comparators are characterized by the design of their components, which consists of: a supporting rod or stand, a sensitive contact or tip, a measuring system that transmits mechanical motion, a means of displaying or indicating the measurement, and sometimes an anvil or a reference surface. The contact tip, measuring system, and display are incorporated into the dial indicator.

Basic Dial Indicators

The basic dial indicator is the simplest form of mechanical contact comparator. It is used to measure a linear dimension, or a variation from a reference dimension. A dial indicator consists of a metal case that serves as a rigid frame to protect the instrument mechanism. This case supports a means of amplifying mechanical motion, a graduated dial, and a protective crystal held in a bezel. The common names of the various parts and features of a dial indicator are given in Fig. 6-1. In the type shown in Fig. 6-1, the spindle is parallel to the dial face. In another type, the spindle is at right angles to the dial face.

Mechanical motion is amplified by the dial indicator using one or more of three principles: levers, gears, or twisted taut bands, in the order of increasing magnification.

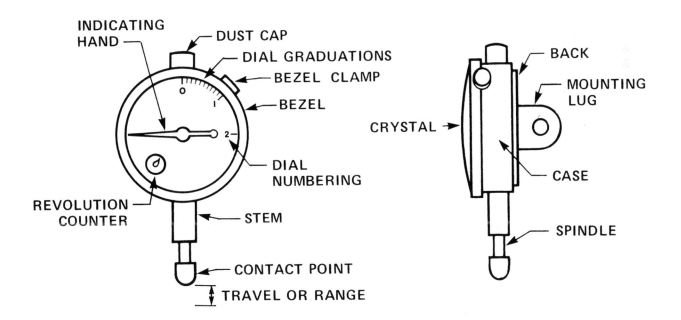

Fig. 6-1 Basic dial indicator components.

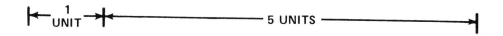

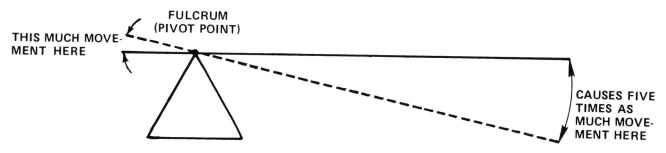

Fig. 6-2   Principle of lever amplification.

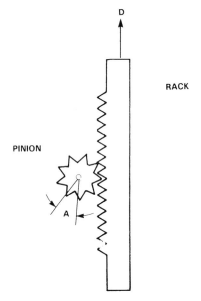

Fig. 6-3   Principle of gear train amplification.

Fig. 6-4   Some gear trains in a dial test indicator.

Lever Mechanisms — Levers are one of the simplest mechanisms for amplifying motion, as shown in the "seesaw" example on Fig. 6-2. Used alone, levers do not usually provide the accuracy, amplification, or sensitivity of other mechanisms. However, because of its simplicity and versatility, the lever is often found in combination with other mechanisms, especially in the universal dial test indicators which will be covered in this chapter.

Gear Mechanisms — Gear train amplification is frequently used in dial indicators, because its accuracy meets the large majority of comparison measurement requirements. In operation, a sensitive contact is attached to a rack (see Figs. 6-3 and 6-4) by a spindle, which transfers the motion to the rack gear. A train of three to five gears magnifies and transmits the movement of the contact to the pinion gear, on which the indicator hand is mounted with a hairspring and take-up gear to eliminate backlash.

The magnification in dial indicators ranges from approximately 40:1 to about 1,500:1. On long-range indicators, additional gears drive revolution counters which count the revolutions of the main hand.

Modifications, combining both spirals and gears, are sometimes employed to change the direction of travel of the contact point with reference to the indicator dial. This is a convenient feature in locating the indicator to suit certain gaging needs.

Twisted Taut Band Magnification — The unique element of this amplification system (see Fig.

6-5A) is a twisted bronze band to which an indicating hand is mounted at the band's centerpoint. Stretching the twisted band tends to straighten it out, causing its centerpoint to rotate. The degree of this rotation is directly proportional to the stretching force applied.

One end of the twisted band is attached to the instrument's frame, the other end to a spring knee. The upper end of the measuring spindle is also attached to the spring knee, so that its upward movement applies stretching force to the band and, in turn, causes the indicating hand to move. Thus, any motion of the measuring spindle, regardless of its magnitude, produces an exactly proportional movement of the indicating hand, amplified by a ratio of up to 200,000:1.

The measuring spindle is suspended between two "frictionless" diaphragm springs (see Fig. 6-5B) which permit it to move up and down freely with no radial play. Because this system does not include bearing or pivot points, no sliding friction is involved.

American National Standard for Dial Indicators

The American National Standards Institute (abbreviated ANSI) has established specifications for the basic dial indicator, to which manufacturers adhere. According to ANSI Standard B89.1.10—1978, all dial indicators (including dial test indicators discussed at the end of this chapter) have least graduations (discrimination units) arranged in four classes of inch values or four classes of metric values, as shown in Fig. 6-6. A particular dial indicator is always marked with the value of its least graduation. Unless otherwise stated, the dial is rotatable and provided with a suitable clamp. ANSI limits the range or travel of the indicator spindle to $2\frac{1}{2}$ revolutions of the indicating hand unless otherwise stated. The indicating hand is set at approximately the 9 o'clock position when the spindle is fully extended. The degree of repetition and accuracy varies with the magnification factor of the dial indicator, and the magnitude of the difference measured. Therefore, the values established in

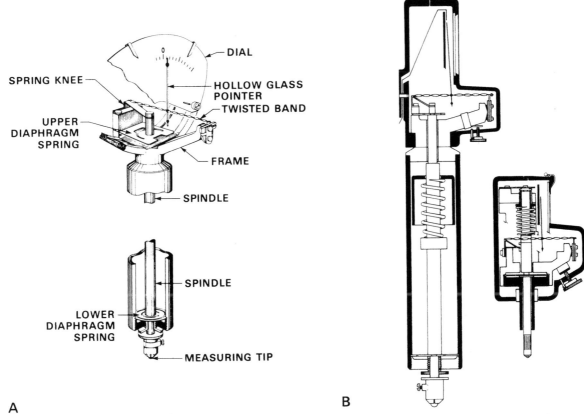

A   B

Fig. 6-5   Operation of twisted taut band magnification. (Courtesy of Federal Products Corporation)

Figure 6-6: ANSI Dial Indicator Specifications.*

Least Graduation		Repeatability	Hysteresis	Accuracy		
				First 2¹/3 Revolutions	First 10 Revolutions	First 20** Revolutions
Inch	mm	Deviation in Least Graduation				
0.00005	0.001	±0.2	0.50	±1	±4	
0.00010	0.002	±0.2	0.50	±1	±3	±4
0.00050	0.010	±0.2	0.33	±1	±3	±4
0.00100	0.020	±0.2	0.33	±1	±2	±4

* From ANSI Standard B89.1.10—1978
** Over 20 revolutions, consult individual manufacturers for their standard practice.

Fig. 6-6 are only maximum tolerances. Readings at any point should be reproducible through successive movements of the spindle to ±¹/₅ graduation. The dial indicator should be accurate to within one graduation, plus or minus, at any point from approximately the 10 o'clock position to the final 2 o'clock position (2¹/₃ turns).

Most manufacturers exceed the ANSI specifications, as well as provide their own modifications to suit particular requirements. For example, indicators are available that have a range of less than 2¹/₂ turns, and many more than 2¹/₂ turns if the hand turns through ten revolutions. Long range indicators (see Fig. 6-7) are usually equipped with small revolution counters.

The discrimination of dial indicators and dial test indicators typically ranges from 0.00005 to 0.001 in. (0.002 to 0.01mm). The total reading capacity of the instrument commonly ranges from 0.003 to 2.000 in. (or 0.2 to 50mm).

Dial Variations — Indicators have either balanced dials or continuous dials—with or without revolution counters. Continuous reading dials are graduated consecutively; that is, the graduations are numbered clockwise from zero to the range included in one complete revolution of the indicating hand (see Fig. 6-8). In balanced dials,

Fig. 6-7 Long-range indicator with revolution counter. (Courtesy of Federal Products Corporation)

Fig. 6-8 Continuous dial face on dial indicator. (Courtesy of Federal Products Corporation)

the graduations start at zero, proceed to the 6 o'clock position on the dial face, and then return to zero. Balanced dials are generally used with bilateral tolerances, such as ±.001, whereas continuous dials are used with unilateral tolerances, such as -.000 and +.002. The revolution counter is used on continuous dial indicators, because one complete revolution of the indicating hand on the continuous dial indicator in Fig. 6-7 registers only 0.100 in. However, if the measurement requires the indicating hand to turn through two or three revolutions, you must use the revolution counter to keep track of the *number of revolutions* that you would multiply by 0.100 to obtain the total measurement. Revolution counters are used on balanced dial indicators for the same basic reason. The indicator hand revolves more rapidly than the eye can count its complete turns, and the revolution counter tells the user which revolution of the indicating hand he is reading.

Although the dial with 100 graduations around its periphery is the most common, other dial scales having 200, 80, 60, 50, 40 or 20 graduations are also used in different designs of dial indicators. The greater number of graduations provides a larger measuring range for the same graduation value (based on the 2½ turns minimum movement), whereas the wider spacing of graduations provides better resolution.

Usually, every tenth graduation is numbered. According to the ANSI standard, numbered graduations always express the travel of the hand on the face of the dial in decimals, either inch or millimeter. Metric dials are usually yellow in color.

Contact Points – Various styles of contact points are available for the most common uses. In addition, many manufacturers stock a great variety of other shapes and sizes to suit special needs. For applications in which they are subject to excessive wear, contact points can be furnished tipped with diamond or tungsten carbide, or be hard chrome plated. The spindle of standard dial indicators has a standard thread bore that mates with the screw shank of interchangeable contact points. Although contact points of many different length are available, the ¼ in. contact point is the most commonly used. Longer contact points are used in restricted

spaces that prevent mounting the indicator close enough to the surface to be measured.

The face of the standard contact point has the shape of a spherical segment with ³⁄₁₆ in. radius. This shape allows essentially single-point contact with most surface forms, and prevents misalignment between the positions of the workpiece and the indicator. Flat end contact points are used to measure diameters on convexly-curved surfaces, such as balls, cylinders, cones, etc. Tapered contact points permit measurements to be made at the bottom of grooves, where the standard contact point cannot penetrate.

Mounting – Dial indicators are mounted either by their stems or by their backs. Mounting the dial indicator by its stem is the more common. Stems are usually round and ³⁄₈ in. in diameter. Metric dial indicators usually have 8mm stem diameters.

Different styles of backs are available for mounting dial indicators (see Fig. 6-9). The centered lug is the most commonly used. The other types of mounting backs are designed to meet special needs.

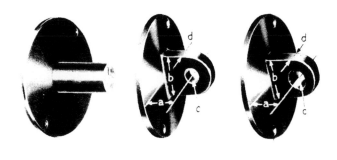

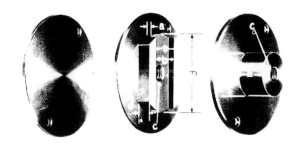

Fig. 6-9 *Indicator backs for various mounting applications. (Courtesy of Federal Products Corporation)*

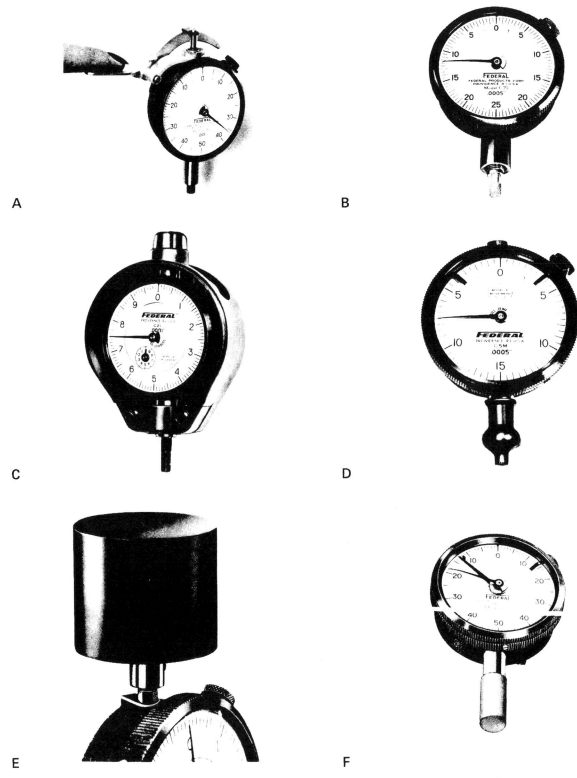

Fig. 6-10   Common dial indicator accessories. (Courtesy of Federal Products Corporation)

Accessories — Various optional accessories (see Fig. 6-10) are available to adapt the dial indicator to particular applications. The most common include:

(1) *Lifting lever* (see Fig. 6-10A) that raises the spindle while placing the part into measured position. This action prevents undue wear on the indicator points, as well as marring of the workpiece surface.

(2) *Bushings* (see Fig. 6-10B) that protect the spindle during clamping.

(3) *Protective housings* (see Fig. 6-10C) to protect the indicator against shock.

(4) *Dust guards* (see Fig. 6-10D) to protect the spindle and bushings under adverse environmental use conditions.

(5) *Weights* (see Fig. 6-10E) that permit precise measurement of compressible materials, such as rubber, textiles, etc., by applying constant pressure directly to the spindle throughout the range of the indicator.

(6) *Auxiliary maximum indicating hand* (see Fig. 6-10F) that attaches beneath the standard indicating hand by means of a magnetic clutch to show maximum reading.

Attachments — The attachments available from manufacturers adapt standard dial indicators to various application requirements. Common attachments include:

(1) *Right angle attachments* (see Fig. 6-11A) that permit the indicator dial to be observed at right angles to the direction of measurement.

(2) *Auxiliary plungers* (see Fig. 6-11B) that attach to the indicator and serve as a precision transfer unit, protecting the spindle bushing from side thrust and severe contact wear. The plungers are available in different lengths.

(3) *Hole attachments* (see Fig. 6-11C) that allow checking internal surfaces and other points which are not accessible to standard dial indicators.

A

B

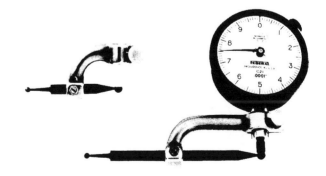

C

Fig. 6-11   Common dial indicator attachments. (Courtesy of Federal Products Corporation)

COMPARATORS AND GAGES—
DIAL INDICATING AND DIGITAL

Many instruments that display a measurement on a built-in dial or a digital readout are used as comparators or gaging devices in the shop. These instruments allow measurements to be made quickly and accurately. Several of them are outgrowths of micrometer and vernier instruments of the same type, but their dials or digital displays are easier to read than their predecessors.

Remember that a common property of all comparators is that they are comparison instruments, and require the use of a master to set the basic measuring position. In this case, the dial indicator will have a balanced dial whose function is to display either coincidence between the master and the part, or the amount and direction of the deviation from the basic size, provided that the deviation is within the measuring range of the instrument.

However, some dial indicating gages are both comparison and direct-reading instruments. When used to make comparative measurements, they are equipped with a balanced dial indicator. When used to make direct measurements, they are equipped with a continuous dial indicator, and sometimes a revolution counter. The direct-reading indicators are usually designed to accommodate ranges and gage capacities of $1/4$, $1/2$, or 1 in. They generally have lifting levers or other mechanisms to raise and lower the contact point.

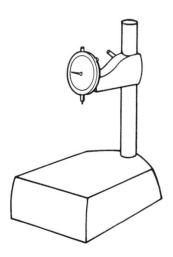

Fig. 6-12   C-frame construction of typical dial indicating bench comparator.

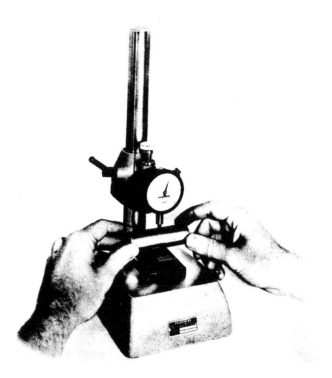

Fig. 6-13   Dial indicating bench comparator. (Courtesy of Federal Products Corporation)

Dial Indicating Bench Comparators

The dial indicating bench comparator consists of a dial indicator attached to an extending arm, attached to a rigid post, attached to a firm reference surface (anvil), as shown in Fig. 6-12. As many setup errors as possible have been eliminated by this fixed design of the bench comparator's components. In use, the indicator is set to zero at the desired dimension with gage blocks or a master cylinder (see Fig. 6-13). Once the indicator has been set to zero, you can check parts for acceptable tolerance using, for example, an indicator equipped with tolerance hands. The tolerance hands are set to the upper and lower limit for part size. A lift mechanism can lift the spindle clear of the workpiece so that the indicator always travels downward to contact the work. This action also helps to compensate for any mechanical error in the comparator setup.

The typical C-frame construction of almost every type of outside diameter measuring instrument or gage, from the vernier caliper up, is used in the bench comparator. Usually, the arm slides up or down the post, and is clamped to it by a screw handle or similar device. This arrangement is comparable to the surface plate and height gage combination described in Chapter V.

The reference anvil of the ordinary comparator is usually machined to the accuracy of a surface plate with regard to flatness, warp, and finish. On very precise comparators, the anvil is usually finished to accuracies in millionths of an inch, comparable to the machinist's flat.

Dial indicators of varying discriminations and equipped with interchangeable contact points and certain accessories can be used on the bench comparator to meet the requirements of specific applications. In addition to the clamping screw handle, many comparator posts are equipped with gear racks so that, by turning a hand wheel, the dial indicator is raised or lowered more easily. Usually this movable apparatus has a fine adjustment screw for the final zeroing of the indicator. Some comparator bench units are equipped with a set of attachable centers for testing roundness, curvature, and warp in cylindrical workpieces. In addition, some anvils have diagonal grooves milled into them, so that dirt, dust, or chips can be scraped into the grooves, thereby keeping the anvil surface as free as possible from the kind of measuring error caused by particles on the measuring surface. V-blocks are used on the anvils of bench comparators, just as they are on surface plates.

Figure 6-14 illustrates the principle of the back stop—a fixture attached to a bench com-

parator (usually to the post) against which the workpiece butts or stops in the correct position under the indicator point. When a back stop is properly adjusted, a cylindrical workpiece will automatically stop at the correct measuring position with the indicator point centered properly over the diameter. This eliminates off-center measurement errors. To set a back stop, first loosen its clamping screw, and move the master or a workpiece under the indicator point until you obtain the "high" indicator reading. Next, bring the back stop into firm contact with the master or sample workpiece, and tighten it in that position. Now, all similar workpieces will be in position for gaging when positioned against the back stop.

Micrometers

Many dial indicating and digital micrometers have been developed in recent years to serve measuring and gaging applications. Among the more important are the dial indicating micrometer, digital readout micrometer, indicating bench micrometer, and internal indicating micrometer.

Dial Indicating Micrometer – The dial indicating micrometer, shown in Fig. 6-15, is similar in operation to a standard micrometer, except that the ten-thousandths reading is read directly from a small indicating dial set into the frame. It has similar accuracy to the vernier micrometer, but can be read faster.

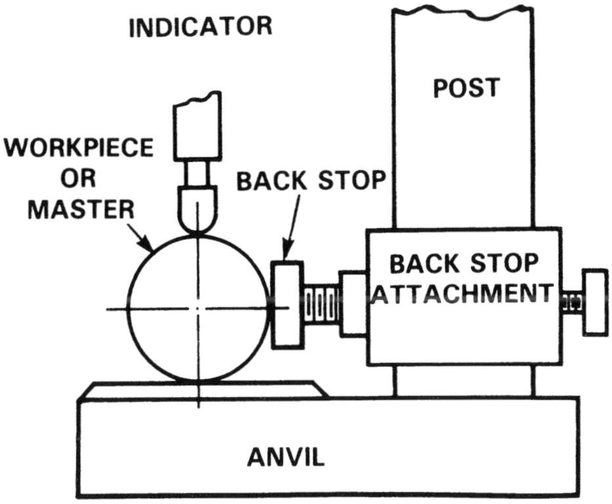

Fig. 6-14   Back stop principle used to accurately position cylindrical pieces.

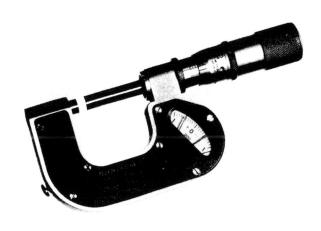

Fig. 6-15   Dial indicating micrometer. (Courtesy of Federal Products Corporation)

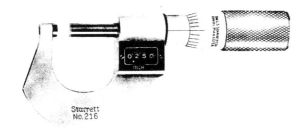

Fig. 6-16 Digital readout micrometer. (Courtesy of The L. S. Starrett Company)

Digital Readout Micrometers — Digital readout micrometers, such as the one shown in Fig. 6-16, are read directly in thousandths from numbers appearing in a counter on the sleeve of the micrometer. Ten-thousandths digital readout micrometers employ a vernier.

Indicating Bench Micrometer — This instrument, shown in Fig. 6-17, is commonly called a "supermicrometer" or a "supermike." It is a precision measuring instrument consisting of a micrometer headstock utilizing a precision screw and a tailstock with adjustable measuring pressures, mounted on a cylindrical bed that provides a measuring range from zero to 10 in. This instrument is suited to applications requiring direct

reading to 0.0001 in. or comparing to 0.00002 in. Direct readings are provided on a digital display, whereas deviation from the comparative master is shown on a calibrated scale.

To use this micrometer for direct measurement, first set both the micrometer head and the digital display to zero or at a nominal 0.100 in. using gage blocks. Next place the part between the anvils of the headstock and tailstock. Then, read the measurement directly off the micrometer head as you would an ordinary micrometer.

To use the supermike as a comparator, first set the micrometer head and digital display to zero. Next, set the micrometer head to the desired dimension to be checked (usually with precision gage blocks). Retract the anvil on the tailstock, and place the workpiece on the table between the two anvils. Now, release the tailstock anvil so that it can contact the workpiece. Finally, read the plus or minus deviation from the desired nominal size on the calibrated scale analog meter.

Fig. 6-17 Indicating bench micrometer. (Courtesy of Pratt & Whitney Machine Tool Division, Measuring Systems Operation)

Fig. 6-18 Indicating bench micrometer for internal measurements. (Courtesy of Pratt & Whitney Machine Tool Division, Measuring Systems Operation)

This instrument is very versatile, and is widely used at the inspection and laboratory levels. It is especially useful in checking cylindrical taper plugs, work thread plugs and pitch diameters using the three-wire method, and workpieces made to high accuracies.

Internal Indicating Micrometer — The internal supermicrometer, shown in Fig. 6-18, is used for direct internal measurement, employing two gaging fingers that contact the part. The one shown has a range of 0.250 in. to 10 in. This instrument includes a vertical adjustment wheel for raising and lowering the gaging fingers referenced from the table top, adjustable gaging pressure, table in-out adjustment, and a table locking knob. Indicators consist of a digital display, zero-center meter, and a vertical finger displacement dial indicator readout.

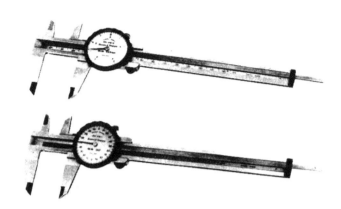

Fig. 6-19   Dial indicating calipers. (Courtesy of Brown & Sharpe Manufacturing Company)

Dial Indicating Calipers

The dial indicating caliper (see Fig. 6-19) is used to make outside, inside, and depth measurements. It is easier to read than the vernier caliper, because you do not need to determine the coincident line of a vernier scale. The indicating hand is operated by a pinion gear that engages a rack on the caliper beam.

The dial indicating caliper is used in exactly the same manner as the vernier caliper except that the fine reading is taken directly from the indicator pointer instead of from a vernier scale. Dial calipers are now more widely used than the older-style vernier calipers since the direct-reading indicator enables them to be read faster and with less likelihood of error in reading. (NOTE: For more on vernier calipers, see Chapter II.)

Dial Depth Gages

The direct-reading dial depth gage shown in Fig. 6-20 is used like the depth gages described in Chapter V, except that it is easier and faster to read. Another type of dial depth gage (see Fig. 6-21) consists of a dial indicator attached to a base that contains an anvil ground to a specific setting depth. This gage is used as a master for making comparative measurements.

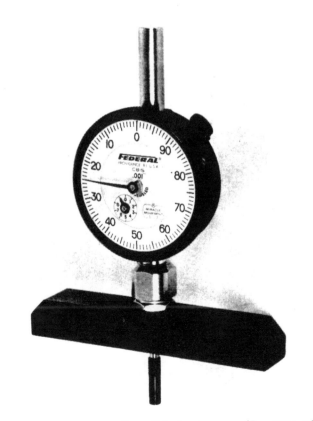

Fig. 6-20   Direct-reading dial depth gage. (Courtesy of Federal Products Corporation)

Fig. 6-21   Dial depth gage used for comparative measurements in gaging. (Courtesy of Federal Products Corporation)

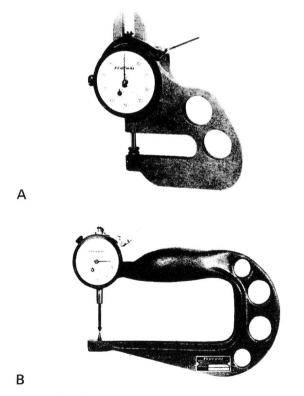

A

B

Fig. 6-22   Dial thickness gages (Courtesy of Federal Products Corporation)

Dial Thickness Gages

Dial thickness gages (see Fig. 6-22) are used to measure small lathe or screw machine parts, the thickness of sheet metal, compressible materials, castings, etc. These are direct-reading portable models, but bench models with anvils are available for both direct and comparative measurements.

Dial Indicating Snap Gages

The dial indicating snap gage (see Fig. 6-23) combines the functions of both the GO and NOT-GO gage into a single instrument, thereby reducing inspection gaging steps from two to one. In addition to accepting or rejecting parts, as fixed snap gages do, dial indicating snap gages also evaluate the actual size of the gaged dimension. This characteristic is very useful in the shop, because it provides feedback for the proper adjustment of machine tools. Dial indicating snap gages are made in different styles, measuring ranges, accuracies, and dial graduations. They are used primarily in production gaging, rather than in toolroom applications.

Dial Bore and Dial Hole Gages

Dial bore and dial hole gages are common names applied to a wide variety of dial instruments used to measure internal diameters. This group of instruments commonly uses two or three-point contact methods to check for size, straightness, and roundness of bores and holes. The smallest hole that can be measured by any of these types of gages is determined by the minimum size of the probe.

Fig. 6-24 A and B show one common type of dial hole gage. The two-point contact is usually used when the hole being inspected is too small to allow the use of a larger gage with a centralizing feature. Some two-point gages feature spring-loaded expanding contacts which help act as self-centralizers. Fig. 6-24 C & D show a gage with another type of centralizing device.

Many of these types of gages have been developed for specific applications such as the cylinder gages covered later in the chapter. These instruments generally require presetting to a master ring gage and will show deviations from the setting on the indicator.

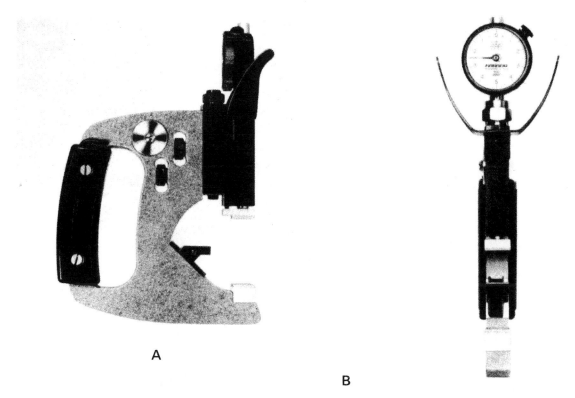

A

B

Fig. 6-23   Dial indicating snap gage, side and front view. (Courtesy of Federal Products Corporation)

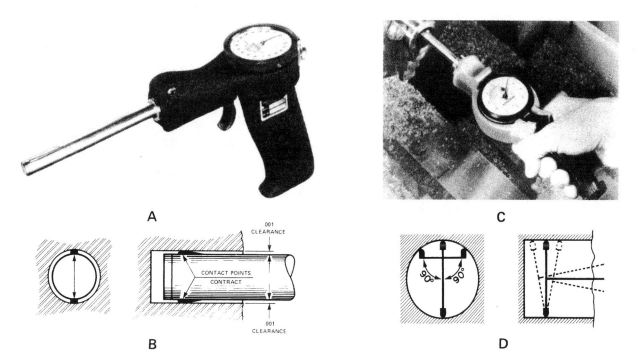

A

C

B

D

Fig. 6-24   A & B) Dial hole gage checks diameter and hole geometry. C & D) Dial bore gage with two-point measuring contact and centralizer. (Courtesy of Federal Products Corporation.)

A

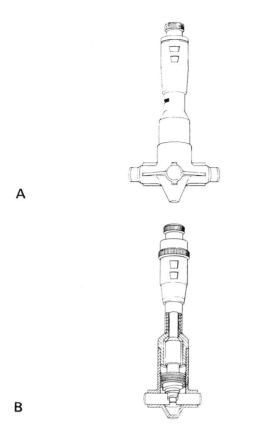

B

Fig. 6-25   *An Intrimik® for measuring size and straightness of a small hole. (Courtesy of Brown & Sharpe Manufacturing Company)*

Small Hole Micrometers

Small hole micrometers use a three point contact system and are self-centering, direct reading, contact gages that measure size and straightness of holes 0.250 in. and larger. They are accurate to ±0.0002 in. even though the discrimination unit is 0.0001 in. or 0.001 mm. The small hole micrometer is less accurate than the dial hole gage and does not measure roundness. It has a primary advantage of speed in taking measurements (see Fig. 6-25) since it does not require setting to a master fixture.

Dial Internal Groove Gages

Dial internal groove gages (see Fig. 6-26) are used to measure the diameter of an internal groove or recess, such as those that hold sealing and retaining rings. Interchangeable jaws are designed for diameters ranging from 0.375 to 6.500 in.

A

B

Fig. 6-26   *Dial internal groove gage with trigger-actuated jaw contact. (Courtesy of Federal Products Corporation)*

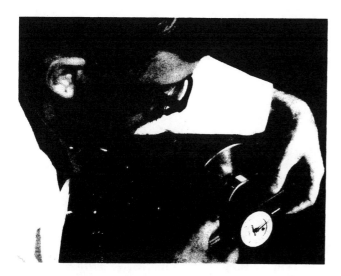

Fig. 6-27   Portable dial indicating ID and OD comparator. (Courtesy of Federal Products Corporation)

A pistol-grip handle allows trigger-actuated retraction and expansion of the jaws, permitting the contacts to be inserted and positioned quickly.

Dial Indicating ID and OD Comparators

The portable ID and OD dial indicating comparator (see Fig. 6-27) can be used to measure both inside and outside diameters simultaneously with two-point measurements directly across the diameter. As shown, they can check work still in the chuck, including slot widths or spacing between flanges. The comparator is set to a gage block master before use. Pneumatic and electronic gage heads are interchangeable with the dial indicator.

Dial Indicating Screw Thread Gages

The dial indicating thread gage (see Fig. 6-28) is used to measure both external and internal screw threads, as well as to make other inside and outside measurements. Instead of screwing into an internal thread, the measuring anvils retract for fast insertion into a threaded hole. The gage is provided with both interchangeable arms and anvils.

Dial Indicating Screw Thread Snap Gages

The dial indicating screw thread snap gage (see Fig. 6-29) is used to measure external screw threads only. Interchangeable anvils allow the

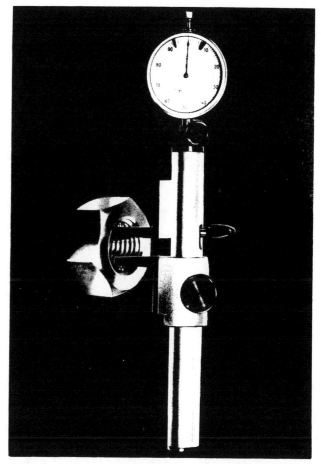

Fig. 6-28   Dial indicating screw thread plug gage. (Courtesy of Mahr Gage Company, Inc.)

Fig. 6-29   Dial indicating screw thread snap gage. (Courtesy of Mahr Gage Company, Inc.)

Fig. 6-30   *Dial base pitch gage. (Courtesy of Mahr Gage Company, Inc.)*

gage to measure the major, minor, and pitch diameter of screw threads ranging from 60 to 3 TPI. A lever on the back of the frame is used to retract the movable anvil.

Dial Base Pitch Gages

The dial base pitch gage (see Fig. 6-30) can be used to make tooth measurements of spur and helical gears with a discrimination of 0.00005 in. This gage will measure gears on or off the gear cutting machine.

Dial Indicating Inprocess Grinding Gages

The dial indicating inprocess grinding gage is used to check cylindrical workpieces while still on the grinder, as shown in Fig. 6-31. In addition to diameters, these gages will check splines, keyways, or fluting, using interchangeable calipers. The gage can also be used with pneumatic, electric, or air-electric magnification. This gage is used primarily in production gaging applications.

A — ON WORK

B — RETRACTED

Fig. 6-31   *Dial indicating in-process grinding gage. (Courtesy of Federal Products Corporation)*

Fig. 6-33   Dial test indicator. (Courtesy of Federal Products Corporation)

DIAL TEST INDICATORS

A dial test indicator, shown in Fig. 6-33, is widely used in setup, inspection, and toolroom work to:

(1)   True and align machine tools, fixtures, and workpieces,

(2)   Inspect and test the trueness of finished work, and

(3)   Compare such linear measurements as height and depth against a master reference and for direct reading of the amount of out of roundness or concentricity.

The dial test indicator differs from the basic dial indicator in the design of its measuring contact. In the basic dial indicator, the contact point is attached to a rigid spindle, whereas in the dial test indicator, the contact point is attached to a lever that swivels.

Various styles and lengths of contact points can be fitted to the dial test indicator body, and any movement of the contact point is transmitted to the dial face by means of a magnifying mechanism. Linear movement of the lever is thereby translated into rotation of the hand over the graduated dial. The scale on the dial reads both to the right and left of zero when properly adjusted to the work, and thus indicates any variation (either plus or minus) from the desired basic dimension.

When either a basic dial indicator or a dial test indicator is fastened to an arm supported by a vertical post and a base, it becomes a shop instrument called a *test set*, as shown in Fig. 6-34. A test set has either a stable base (to prevent tipping), a magnetic base, a surface gage or a base designed to be

Fig. 6-32   Cylinder gage. (Courtesy of The L. S. Starrett Company)

Cylinder Gages

A cylinder gage (see Fig. 6-32) uses a dial indicator to check the internal surfaces of a cylinder for trueness, straightness, roundness, and scoring. The cylinder gage is in the family of dial hole and dial bore gaging.

To check the trueness of a cylinder with this gage, first adjust the contact rods to a dimension slightly greater than the diameter of the cylinder. Then, slip the instrument into the cylinder, with the dial at right angles to the cylinder wall. Next, bring the dial zero point into agreement with the indicating pointer in the same way as you do in using a dial indicator. To check for taper, grasp the handle and traverse the gage from one end of the cylinder to the other. The amount of pointer variation from zero indicates the amount of taper. (The graduations on the dial are in thousandths of an inch.) Out-of-roundness can be detected and measured by rotating the instrument at selected points within the cylinder.

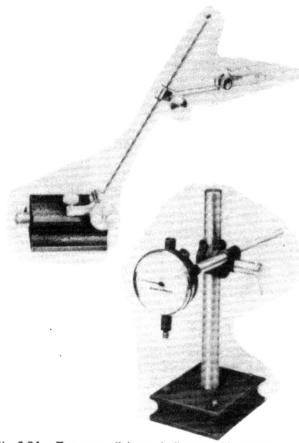

Fig. 6-34   Test sets: dial test indicator with surface gage on the left, dial indicator with a base stand on the right. (Courtesy of Brown & Sharpe Manufacturing Company)

clamped to a surface plate. When a test set is used with a surface plate, the first step is to wring together a stack of gage blocks equal to the dimension being checked, and then zero the test indicator to it. Next, remove the gage block stack, and try the workpiece under the test set indicator. Whatever the indicator reads, plus or minus from zero, shows how much larger or smaller the workpiece is compared to the master, or gage block stack, in this case. Instead of gage blocks, you can also use a micrometer height gage to zero the test indicator.

The dial test indicator itself is usually provided with a holding bar and service clamp designed to fit the measuring arm and clamp of a surface gage or height gage. The universal swivel allows the dial test indicator to be set at almost any angle or extended position. When used with a vernier height gage, the dial test indicator is attached to the sliding arm. However, the contact point of the indicator will not be at the same height above the surface plate as the surface of the height gage's sliding arm. Therefore, you cannot use the vernier height gage for direct scale reading in this case. Instead, the height gage becomes a test set used to compare a height to a known master, such as a stack of gage blocks.

One important application of such an indicating height gage is in checking shaft conditions, for example, concentricity. Suppose that you must determine whether or not one shaft diameter is concentric with another diameter on the same shaft within a specified tolerance. Several conditions can affect concentricity: our-of-roundness, bent shaft, shaft curvature, and eccentricity.

A non-precise check for out-of-roundness is first to place the shaft horizontally against the vertical surface of a right angle plate. Then place the height gage indicator point (test set) over the part, and rotate the part slowly. Any deviation of the needle on the dial will indicate the amount of out-of-roundness.

Greater precision in checking for out-of-roundness is to place one end of the shaft in a V-block, as shown in Fig. 6-35A. Place the height gage and indicator over the shaft section, and revolve the shaft section in the V-block. The indicator will register any out-of-roundness present in that section. Repeat the procedure on other sections of the shaft, as necessary.

However, the most accurate check for out-of-roundness (roundness) is a master spindle (see Fig. 6-36). The part is placed on the face plate of the spindle and indicated in until the best reading of roundness can be obtained. Parts can be measured to an accuracy of 0.000005 in. with this method.

To check for a bent shaft, first place the shaft on a V-block, as shown in Fig. 6-35B. Next, place the indicator contact point at two locations along the shaft diameter. A difference in readings between the two locations indicates a bent shaft if neither portion is tapered. Now, rotate the shaft one-quarter turn, and repeat the check. Any change in the readings indicates a bent shaft rather than taper or out-of-roundness.

To check for shaft curvature (straightness), first place the part on two V-blocks with about 1/4 in. of each end of the shaft resting on each, as shown in Fig. 6-35C. Move the indicating gage over

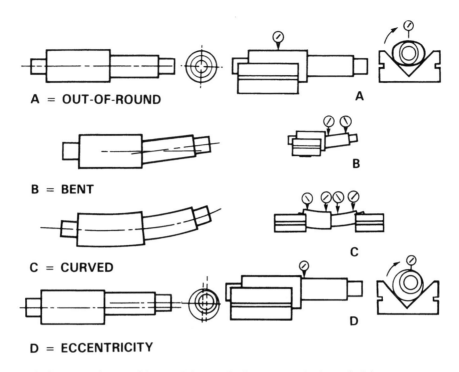

A = OUT-OF-ROUND

B = BENT

C = CURVED

D = ECCENTRICITY

Fig. 6-35   Checking shaft conditions with a dial test indicator attached to a height gage.

the part and set the dial for a zero reading. Then take three readings around the shaft, rotating the shaft about 90° each time. Repeat this procedure at several locations along the shaft to separate bent or curved shaft conditions from other conditions.

Fig. 6-36   A master spindle checks roundness and plots error on chart to an accuracy of 0.000005 in. (Courtesy of Mahr Gage Co.)

The final check is to measure eccentricity between one section of a shaft and another. First, place the large diameter of the shaft in a V-block, as shown in Fig. 6-35D. Then, place the indicator over the small section, close to the shoulder. Revolve the shaft in the V-block, and note any deviations. As an additional check, place the small diameter in the V-block, and repeat the procedure.

CARE OF DIAL INDICATORS

Dial indicators (and some dial test indicators) are precision instruments having sensitive mechanisms that require even more care than you must give to the other precision instruments you have learned about so far. To retain their accuracy, follow these guidelines for proper dial indicator care.

Keep the reference surface clean and level. A test set base should be clean and seated positively. Many erroneous readings are caused by a surface plate or anvil that is not perfectly clean and level.

Mount the indicator securely to the fixture or holding device. You can use ordinary wrenches and tools to secure the mounting. Avoid even a slight wobble, or you will obtain inaccurate gaging and parts.

Mount dial indicators close to the support posts on test sets or comparators, thereby avoiding deflection of the holding arm. Also, keep support posts as short as possible, because support deflection will not be uniform over a succession of tests, and there is no constant you can use to compensate for it.

Do not clamp the indicator against the stem with the set screw. Instead, equalize the pressure with a split clamping device. Too much pressure will make the spindle bind, resulting in a sluggish, sticky indicator. If necessary, use a stem adapter with special threaded-stem indicators for stem support.

Handle the gage so that it can seat itself on the workpiece. Be sure to hold it lightly—too much pressure will affect any gage. Rest the weight of the gage and your hand on the fixed or reference contact. Otherwise these weights will affect the accuracy and consistency of the gage.

Do not lock the indicator in position until you have set it carefully under proper gage tension—that is, at least one quarter turn from its "at rest" position. In the standard movement, the pointer at rest is set at the 9 o'clock position so that it will be under the proper tension at zero.

Do not tighten contact points or adapters too far against the rack spindle. Strain will cause distortion, make the spindle bind and the mechanism stick, or cause the guidepin to loosen or shear off.

Use diamond, tungsten carbide, or hard chromium tipped indicator contact points whenever the contacts will be subjected to heavy wear or abrasion.

Test all your indicators under gaging conditions at intervals during the operating day. You can do this by gaging a part twice, then comparing the readings to make sure the setting has not changed. Use a master part or gage blocks, as you would to test the accuracy of any other precision instrument. Do not try to test accuracy under gaging conditions by simply pushing in the contact point and noting whether the return point is constant.

Do not subject indicators to any hard, sudden blows. Take care when you use them to check work in process, such as on a lathe. If blows are unavoidable, use a shock-proof indicator.

Make use of the indicator accessories that will make your dial indicators more efficient, more adaptable, and more versatile. For example, use lifting levers, right angle attachments, maximum-point hands, and weights for measuring compressible materials as the conditions call for them.

Clean indicator dials with soap and water, benzene, or a soft rubber eraser.

Inspect dial indicators often, especially if they are exposed to oil or other fluids that turn sticky. Inspection frequency depends on the type of gaging and the presence of dust, vapors, oils, etc. If an indicator is used intermittently under clean conditions, inspect it externally, and test it daily with a master. Under unfavorable conditions, let your experience and judgment govern the period of time between inspections (for example, frequent cleaning is necessary if the indicator is used near acid, heat, or cleaning fluid). Have authorized personnel make internal inspections of all indicators after each production job or every 6 months, whichever is shorter. If internal cleaning is needed, follow the manufacturer's instructions.

Keep the indicator spindle clean by wiping it with a soft, lint-free cloth. Remove all dirt and abrasive material from the spindle to prevent wear and to keep the spindle from sticking in its bearings. Before gaging, wipe the contact point and workpiece surfaces to remove dust, oil, and chips.

Do not oil spindle bearings except under special conditions. Oil the movement bearings using watch oil applied by a thin wire. A dial indicator needs little oil—a drop is about 20 times too much. Do not use oil that tends to corrode or get gummy. Never use grease.

Do not oil an indicator that has been idle for some time. If the spindle sticks, work it in and out by hand until it slides freely on its own bearings.

Do not use an indicator that has been dropped or stuck until you have tested it thoroughly. Test it on a bench comparator set or some other supporting device to make sure it's precisely calibrated. Then re-set the indicator in position as precisely as you set it the first time.

Do not use a dial indicator for anything except what it is intended for—accurate gaging. It is not a jackhammer or paperweight. It won't give good service unless you treat it properly with the same kind of care you give to your other precision instruments.

Do not drill holes in the indicator's back or

case. Chips will get inside and ruin the movement. Manufacturers can supply proper backs for most applications.

Store your dial indicators in a safe, dry place and cover them to keep the dust out. Cushioning them is not necessary, but storage should protect them from being scratched or bumped by other tools—and against corrosion from moisture.

CHAPTER VI REVIEW

1. How do thin, vane-type pointers help reduce error caused by parallax?

2. Why can't optical comparators be used to their greatest advantage on highly-finished parts?

3. Describe the difference between a dial test indicator and a dial indicator.

4. What is a test set?

5. True or False: To allow for the Earth's rotation, dial indicators should be adjusted to zero each day at 9:00 A.M.

6. How can a dial indicator be spot-checked under actual gaging conditions? How often should this be done.

7. Explain how hysteresis-type errors can occur in a dial indicator. How much of this type error is permitted under ANSI standards?

8. Why is a dial indicating caliper easier to read than a vernier caliper?

9. Explain how to use dial indicating instruments to check concentricity of several diameters on a single shaft.

10. Practice and demonstrate to the satisfaction of your supervisor or instructor the correct and accurate use and care of dial indicators and other indicating gages and mechanical comparators.

Chapter VII

Pneumatic, Electrical, Electronic, and Optical Comparators

The high accuracy requirements of precision machined interchangeable parts have led to the development and extensive shop use of semiautomatic gages and measurement systems ,that require—but considerably reduce—manual skills, and thus contribute markedly to greater inspection accuracy and lower overall inspection costs.

PNEUMATIC COMPARATORS

Pneumatic comparators, commonly called *air gages*, were first used in France before 1930 for production gaging of carburetor jets. Prior to World War II, air gages were used in the United States on a limited basis for bore gaging. However, when the United States became involved in the War, the need for large numbers of ordnance devices created a demand for reliable gaging that could be used in production by persons with little mechanical training or skills. To meet this requirement, gage manufacturers applied pneumatic systems to numerous internal gaging applications. This type of gaging system proved to be very successful, and its use increased substantially through the period from 1942 to 1945. Following the War, many industries, such as automotive and bearing manufacturers, continued to use pneumatic gaging systems for their consumer products. At the present time, pneumatic gaging is one of the major production gaging methods in use. Although it provides greater amplification than the mechanical comparator system, it has less range.

A pneumatic gaging system consists basically of elements that provide a constant pressure air supply, an indicating means, and a metering orifice or nozzle. The principle of its operation is based on the effects of varying the flow of air as it exits from the metering nozzle. Three primary types of pneumatic circuits are used in pneumatic gaging systems: back pressure, free flow, and differential.

Back Pressure Circuit

As shown in Fig. 7-1A, a back pressure pneumatic circuit consists of a nozzle fixed in position in relation to a stop or jig. Compressed air at constant supply passes through a restriction in the line of flow (building up a steady back pressure), and discharges through the nozzle. The amount of the nozzle back pressure at P depends on the size of the gap G between the measured surface and the nozzle opening. If the measured dimension D increases, then G decreases, restricting the discharge of air and increasing P. Conversely, if D decreases, P decreases. Thus, the pressure gage indicates deviation of the dimension from some preset value. The pressure is directly proportional to the deviation, limited to a few thousandths of an inch span.

For example, as flow from the nozzle is obstructed, pressure in the system builds up to the regulated value, and air flow through the system drops. Over a significant range of values in such a gaging system, a linear relationship exists between flow or pressure and the size of the

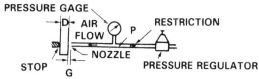

A = BACK PRESSURE PNEUMATIC CIRCUIT REQUIRES A
RESTRICTION TO MAKE COMPARISON MEASUREMENTS

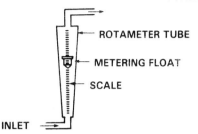

B = ROTAMETER REPLACES RESTRICTION IN FREE FLOW
PNEUMATIC CIRCUIT

*Fig. 7-1   Back pressure (A) and free flow (B) pneumatic
circuit principles.*

nozzle. In many gaging applications, the linear
relationship is equal to the clearance that separates
the nozzle and an obstruction. The indicating
element then shows the change in flow or pressure
as a linear measurement.

The obstruction can be either the workpiece
being gaged or an integral part of the gage head.
An example of when the workpiece itself serves
as the obstruction is in the gaging of a bore. In
this case, the gage head or spindle inserted into the
bore has two opposing jets through which air is
flowing. No contact is made between the gage
head and the part being measured, because the
closeness of fit serves as the obstruction. When the
obstruction is part of the gage head, the gage
spindle includes a component that mechanically
contacts the work being measured. Movement
of this component in relation to a sized orifice
affects air flow, and establishes the basis for
measurement. These air gaging systems are extremely sensitive (better than 0.0001 in. or
0.003mm), rugged, and—when periodically calibrated against a standard—very accurate. Any
number of nozzles can be used in a jig to check
many kinds of dimensions.

Free Flow Circuit

In the free flow type of pneumatic circuit,
the flow of air is measured by a rotameter instead

A

B

*Fig. 7-2   Free flow pneumatic gaging system and circuit.
(Courtesy of Bendix Automation & Measure-
ment Division)*

of by back pressure. A rotameter (see Fig. 7-1B) consists of a tapered glass metering tube and a float, plus inlet and outlet connections. The float is positioned inside the tapered tube by the pressure of air flowing up through the tube. In this circuit, the flow restriction is the annular area between the float and the tube (the annular area obviously increases as the float rises). The pressure differential is fixed, determined by the weight of the float and the buoyant forces. Thus, the rotameter can be calibrated for direct reading by etching a scale on the surface of the glass tube, as shown in Fig. 7-2.

Differential Circuit

The differential system is a variation of the original back pressure system that uses a parallel circuit, as shown in Fig. 7-3. In this system, air under constant pressure enters two separate channels. The air in the reference channel escapes to the atmosphere through the adjustable zero restrictor, while the air in the measuring channel escapes to the atmosphere through the jets of the gage head. The two channels are bridged by a very precise quick-response indicating meter that reflects any differential in air pressure between the two channels. This bridged system is similar to the familiar electrical Wheatstone Bridge, described later in this chapter.

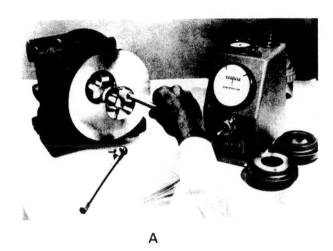

A

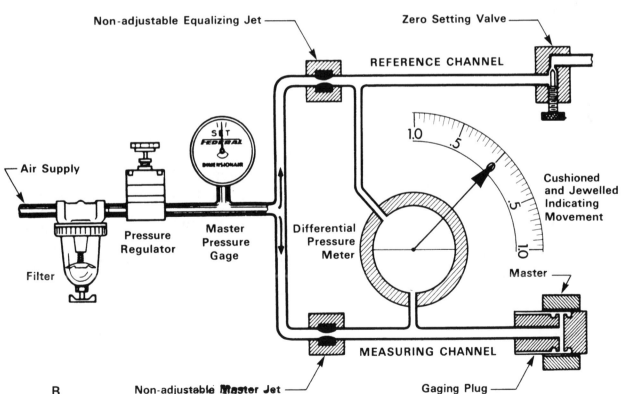

B

Fig. 7-3   Differential pneumatic gaging system and circuit. (Courtesy of Federal Products Corporation)

The advantages of pneumatic gaging include:

(1) Many part dimensions and relationships can be gaged without contact between the nozzle surface and the part surface.

(2) The high-velocity airstream removes coolant or other loose contamination, and impinges directly on the surface for an accurate reading of part size.

(3) A diameter reading can be made directly in line with the nozzles, whereas axial or rotary movement of the nozzles in the bore can detect any deviation in size.

(4) The direct nozzle air plug has no moving parts, thereby eliminating any friction that could affect readings.

(5) The air plug sensor can be connected with a flexible extension several feet in length to the instrument portion of the pneumatic circuit, which is extremely useful for machine gaging applications.

(6) Several dimensions can be gaged simultaneously.

(7) The high sensitivity of pneumatic gaging allows determination of size in increments as small as 0.000010 in. (.00025mm).

One major limitation of pneumatic gaging is its requirement for absolutely clean, dry air supplied to the gage circuit. Any contaminants that enter the instrument or gage member can alter the zero setting or the amplification. Consequently, the gage circuitry must be monitored regularly with setting master rings.

A second limitation of pneumatic gaging is that part surface characteristics can affect the gaging results. For example, roughness or porosity can cause an averaging effect of the air impinging against the part surface. As a result, the pneumatic gage may indicate a size that is larger than the actual size.

Although it has some limitations, pneumatic gaging is a very important method for gaging the diameters of holes and bores, and to check relationships, such as squareness, concentricity, parallelism, center distance, straightness, flatness, thickness, and clearance and interference (match gaging).

Fig. 7-4   Pneumatic plug gage. (Courtesy of Federal Products Corporation)

Fig. 7-5   Pneumatic ring gage. (Courtesy of Federal Products Corporation)

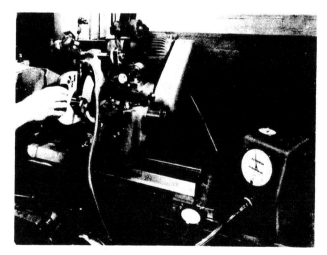

Fig. 7-6   Pneumatic snap gage. (Courtesy of Federal Products Corporation)

Gage Heads

Three styles of gage heads are used in pneumatic gaging systems: plug, ring, or snap (see Fig. 7-4, 7-5 and 7-6). These gage heads measure by one of two methods:

(1) Direct—using an open jet or jets with no mechanical contact made between gage head and part, or

(2) Indirect—using an intermediate gage head component that mechanically contacts the part.

Direct measuring gage heads — Direct measuring gage heads have from one to six jets, depending on their purposes.

Single-jet plugs (see Fig. 7-7A) are used to check concentricity, location, squareness, flatness, straightness, length, and depth, as shown in Fig. 7-8.

Two-jet plugs (see Fig. 7-7B) are used to check inside diameters, out-of-roundness, bell mouth, and taper, as shown in Fig. 7-9. A common dual-jet gage plug is shown in Fig. 7-10. This gage head contains two opposing jets for measuring true diameter. By traversing and rotating the spindle as the hole is probed, out-of-round, bell mouth, hourglass, barrel shape, and diameter can be determined.

Three-jet plugs (see Fig. 7-7C) are used to check triangular out-of-round or lobing.

Four-jet plugs (see Fig. 7-7D) are used for average diameter readings of an ID or an OD.

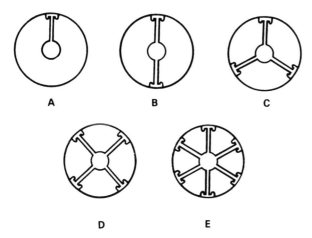

Fig. 7-7   *Direct measuring gage head designs. (Courtesy of Federal Products Corporation)*

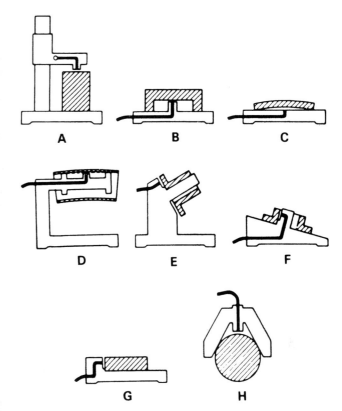

Fig. 7-8   *Applications of single-jet tooling: (A) height, (B) depth, (C) flatness, (D) camber or "banana" shape, (E) and (F) squareness of long and short bores, (G) face squareness, and (H) outside diameter (OD). (Courtesy of Bendix Automation & Measurement Division)*

Six-jet plugs (see Fig. 7-7E) are used to show average readings of three diameters. This design tends to average out two- and three-point out-of-round.

Indirect measuring gage heads — Indirect measuring gage heads use intermediate components such as plungers, balls, blades, and leaf springs (see Fig. 7-11) to contact part surfaces.

Plunger-type gage heads are called *air cartridges* (see Fig. 7-12). Air cartridges consist of a spring-actuated plunger that serves as a precision valve stem to regulate the amount of air flowing through a jet. Any change in the plunger position changes the airflow and the consequent reading on the indicator. The maximum and minimum limits of plunger travel are set with leaf masters. Different models gage tolerances as small as 0.0001 in. to as wide as 0.100 in. or more. Generally, 2000:1

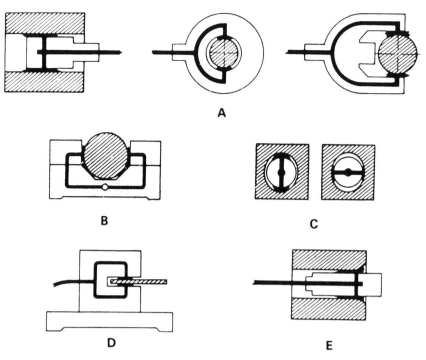

Fig. 7-9   Applications of two-jet tooling: (A) true diameter, (B) outside diameter in vee, (C) out-of-round, (D) thickness, and (E) bell-mouth. (Courtesy of Bendix Automation & Measurement Division.)

amplification is used. The type of indicating scale is determined by application. Most plunger-type air cartridges are used with free flow type gages. Examples of air cartridge applications are shown in Fig. 7-13.

Setting Masters

Setting masters are used to establish the maximum and minimum tolerance limits on a pneumatic comparator. Air plugs are normally set with

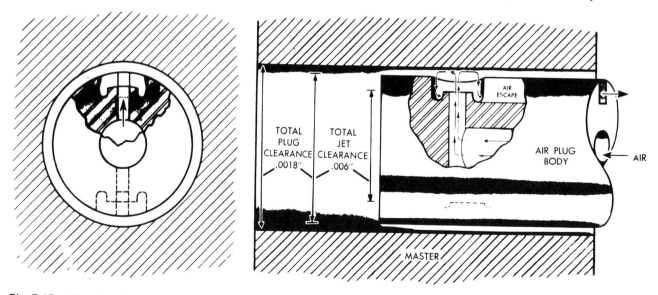

Fig. 7-10   Two-jet plug gage operation and cross section. (Courtesy of Federal Products Corporation)

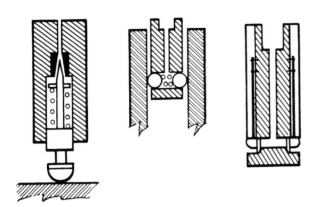

Fig. 7-11   Indirect measuring gage head designs.

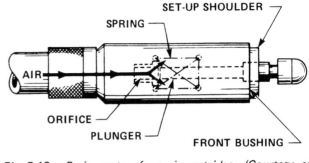

Fig. 7-12   Basic parts of an air cartridge. (Courtesy of Bendix Automation & Measurement Division)

rings, whereas air rings and air snap gages can be set with either disks or cylindrical plugs (see Fig. 7-14). The use of two masters is preferred in setting an air gage, because it ensures that the gage is functioning at both toleranced limits (maximum and minimum).

In the free-flow-type of comparator, the scale pointers are set to the tolerance limits by placing the masters on the gage head alternately, and adjusting the float position to each master by turning knobs at the base of the instrument until the top of the float is directly opposite the corresponding limit pointer.

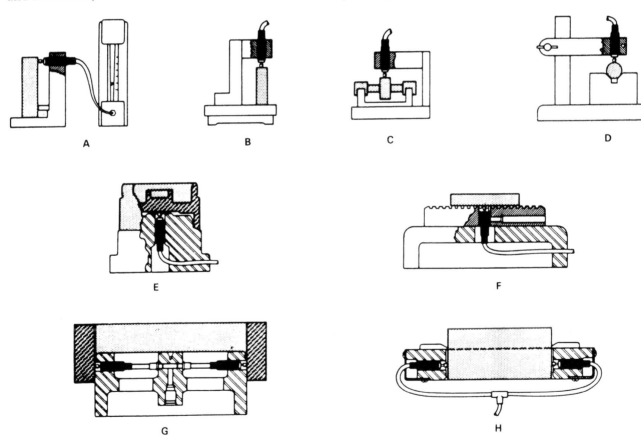

Fig. 7-13   Air cartridge applications: (A) squareness, (B) height, (C) concentricity, (D) 3-point OD, (E) depth, (F) flatness, (G) inside diameter (ID), and (H) outside diameter (OD).

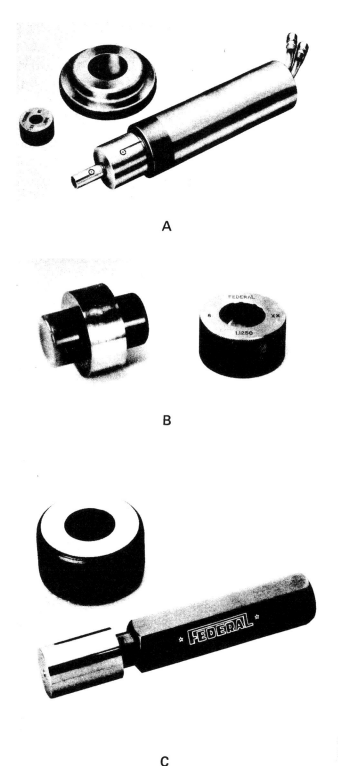

A

B

C

Fig. 7-14   Setting masters: (A) rings, (B) disk, and
(C) plug. (Courtesy of Federal Products
Corporation)

Indirect measuring gage heads are set using a calibrator and gage blocks, plus air cartridges with minimum and maximum "feelers" or calibration leaf masters.

ELECTRICAL AND ELECTRONIC COMPARATORS

Electrical and electronic comparators detect, measure, and display very small variations in the dimensions of a part. In operation, the dimensional variation displaces a mechanically-contacting gaging head in relation to a preset position, thereby generating proportional electrical signals that are then amplified and either indicated or recorded. The indication generally appears on the face of a meter whose scale is graduated in fractional values of the standard units of length, the inch or the millimeter.

The basic principle of converting mechanical displacement into proportional electrical variations was originally applied to electrical gages designed to make linear measurements in very fine increments. However, the invention of the vacuum tube and—more importantly—the development of solid-state devices, such as transistors and integrated circuits, made possible gaging systems that are superior to the original electrical comparators. Solid-state devices, which have almost completely replaced the electron tube in measuring instrumentation, have nearly replaced plain electrical gages in most applications. A single electronic integrated circuit of very small size can contain several thousand circuit elements.

Electric and electronic comparators are widely used in gaging the dimensions of parts, because they provide almost instantaneous response, and their output can be used to perform work (display and/or control). They also offer a choice of amplifying means by switching, electrical zeroing, or differential gaging. Electronic gaging can achieve exceptionally high amplification—as high as 100,000:1. The main difference between electric and electronic gages is one of amplification and type of output.

Both electric and electronic gaging systems consist of three elements:

(1) The transducer which measures a variable, converts information about the variable to an electrical quantity (usually a variable

voltage), and transmits the electrical signal,

(2) A device that amplifies or otherwise modifies the electrical output of the transducer, and

(3) An indicator or control element that indicates the measurement on a scale and/or controls a recording instrument.

In electrical and electronic gaging systems, displacement of the gage head can be measured electrically by its effect on the resistance, inductance, or capacitance, of an appropriate sensing element. Therefore, these systems incorporate precision ON-OFF switches, various types of bridge circuits and linear-variable-differential transformers (LVDTs) as the primary element in the transducer. To understand how these important elements work, let us briefly review electrical circuits, the function and types of switches, and the types of bridge circuits used in electrical and electronic comparators: Wheatstone, capacitance, inductance, and impedance. You will learn about LVDTs later in this chapter.

Electric/Contact Gages

Electric/contact gages are very similar in appearance to the mechanical dial indicator and the mechanical comparator (see Fig. 7-15 and 7-16), differing mainly in that the indicator rack spindle is designed to actuate electric precision limit switches. The switches, in turn, initiate lights to indicate dimensional classification and/or actuate sorting and corrective mechanisms.

Electric/contact gages, such as the one shown in Fig. 7-15, usually contain two sets of contacts similar to a single-pole double-throw switch. One set of closed contacts may represent and indicate an oversize workpiece, whereas the second set of contacts—when closed—may indicate undersize. When neither set of contacts close, good or within-size workpieces are indicated. The position at which these contacts open and close a circuit is adjustable to accommodate various workpiece tolerances. Switching accuracy within approximately 0.000025 in. is attained by this electric/contact gage derived directly from the spindle. However, a magnification of only about 2:1 is derived from the lever ratio of the switches.

Another type of electric/contact gage, shown in Fig. 7-16, is used to save operator time in

classifying work dimensionally. The indicating lights show the true classifications instantaneously and accurately, and the dial shows the specific size of the part when this information is needed.

Like a dial indicator, the electric/contact gage is usually set to a master or dimensional standard, and is available with dials graduated in 0.001, 0.005, or 0.0001 in.

The amount of current used in the electric circuits is important in maintaining the accuracy of the switch. If the current causes arcing to occur at the switch contacts, the contacts will burn or erode and effectively change their relative position. This, in turn, will change the accuracy of the switch. The recommended minimum gaging tolerance when using the electric/contact gages is a total of 0.0005 in. They are best suited to situations in which extreme precision is not a prime factor, and where electric limits are required at minimum cost.

Inductance-Bridge-Circuit Gages

Inductance-bridge-circuit gages are usually used when higher amplification is necessary than can be achieved with the electric/contact gage. The system usually consists of three basic components: (1) the gage head, (2) the power supply unit, and (3) the indicator.

Mechanical contact with the workpiece is used to position a reed-floated armature between a pair of coils. This arrangement effectively changes the reactance in a Wheatstone bridge circuit. Reactance is the opposition offered to the flow of ac current by *pure* inductance or capacitance in a circuit. The resulting imbalance can then be read directly on a suitably calibrated galvanometer-type indicating meter. This system provides variable resistances, making it possible to shift zero position electrically, and to vary the amplification of the system. Variations in part size as small as 0.000025 in. can be read directly on the indicating meter without auxiliary amplification. Inductance-bridge-circuit gages are generally used for close-tolerance work and for automatic gaging and sorting machines.

Electronic Circuits

For an electric circuit to be classified as an electronic circuit, some of its components must be

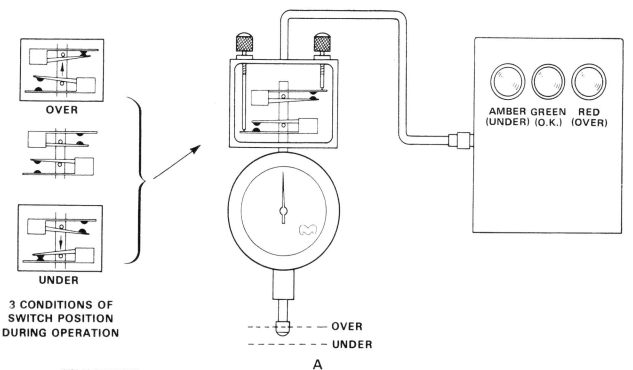

OVER

UNDER

**3 CONDITIONS OF
SWITCH POSITION
DURING OPERATION**

AMBER GREEN RED
(UNDER) (O.K.) (OVER)

—————— OVER

—————— UNDER

A

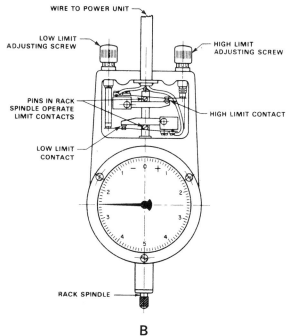

WIRE TO POWER UNIT

LOW LIMIT
ADJUSTING SCREW

HIGH LIMIT
ADJUSTING SCREW

PINS IN RACK
SPINDLE OPERATE
LIMIT CONTACTS

HIGH LIMIT CONTACT

LOW LIMIT
CONTACT

RACK SPINDLE

B

*Fig. 7-15   Electrical gaging system (A). The switching
mechanism is spindle-operated. Two independent sets of contacts permit three switching
conditions for classifying parts into "over,"
"good," and "under." Electric-contact gage
head (B). (Courtesy of Federal Products
Corporation)*

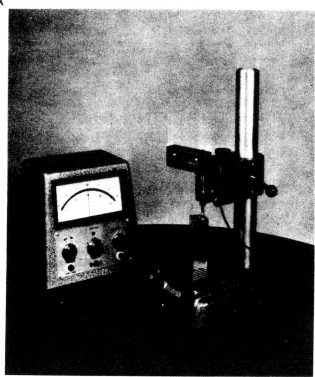

*Fig. 7-16   Electric comparator gage being used to compare
a precision gage block dimension with that of
a cylindrical gage being inspected. (Courtesy
of DoAll Company)*

able to switch currents or voltages without the use of mechanical switches, or to amplify or control voltages or currents without either a mechanical or nonelectrical command. Electronic components include such devices as electron tubes, transistors, magnetic amplifiers, diodes, quartz crystals, resistors, capacitors, inductors, transformers, and ferrite devices.

Complex solid-state electronic systems often contain assemblies of components interconnected on a chip as subassemblies. The most elaborate of these subassemblies, called *integrated circuits*, are collections of both active and passive components formed by deposition, diffusion, or crystalline growth on a common poorly-conducting (or insulating) surface. Integrated circuits (ICs) provide many practical advantages compared with circuits composed of separate components, as well as several disadvantages. The most important advantage is the size of the extremely small chip that can support a relatively complex circuit. For example, an operational amplifier having a gain in the tens of thousands or more can be housed in a single transistor package whose volume is on the order of 0.1 in.^{3}. Older equivalent tube-type designs typically required more than 10 in.^{3} of space. The time required by an IC to transmit a signal is also less by as much as two or more orders of magnitude compared with those of corresponding tube circuits, because lead lengths can be reduced from many inches to as little as a few thousandths of an inch in a typical IC.

Electronic Amplifiers

The solid-state electronic amplifiers that amplify the power level of a physical quantity in modern electronic gaging systems depend upon transistors for their operation. A few electronic amplifiers are magnetic amplifiers, whereas most are in the form of rotating electrical machinery. Since it was invented in 1947, the transistor has become very important as an active circuit element in amplifiers. Most amplifiers use transistors because of their low cost, long life, high reliability, better overall characteristics, and small size, and also because the physical configuration of the transistor makes possible circuits that are not practical using vacuum tubes.

Electronic Gage Heads

The three basic types of electronic gage heads are the lever, reed spring, and cartridge or plunger-type. The three types are usually interchangeable with each other in a given electronic gaging system, and are selected according to the nature of the application.

The lever-type gage head resembles a dial test indicator head, and is used with height gages or with similar support stands or fixtures to make measurements on a surface plate (see Fig. 7-17). Its spindle tip has pivot suspension, allowing access to work surfaces that cannot be reached by the axial-displaced cartridge-type head.

The reed-spring-type electronic gage head (see Fig. 7-18) is a friction-free device used in high-precision electronic comparator applications. Its contact block is mounted with reed suspension, providing sensitive frictionless response to the axial displacement motion of the spindle.

The cartridge or plunger-type electronic gage head (see Fig. 7-19) is basically a cylinder having an 0.375 in. OD. This is the ANSI standard diameter for dial indicator stems, and permits the two types of heads to be interchanged on fixtures designed to operate with a dial indicator. The spindle of the electronic cartridge has axial displacement, like the reed-spring-type, but the suspension is either by spring steel disks, or a helical spring controlled by a guide bushing.

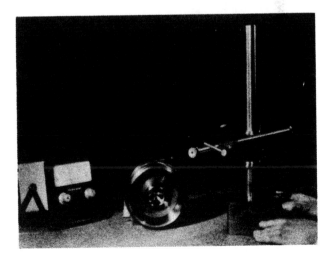

Fig. 7-17 Lever-type electronic gage head mounted on an indicator holder for surface plate work. (Courtesy of Federal Products Corporation)

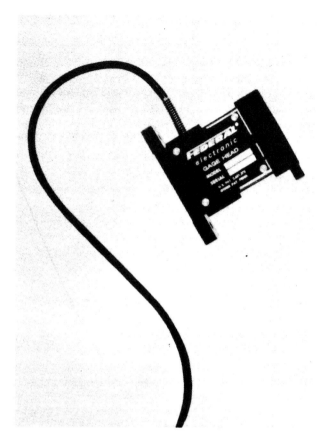

Fig. 7-18   Reed-spring-type electronic gage head. (Courtesy of Federal Products Corporation)

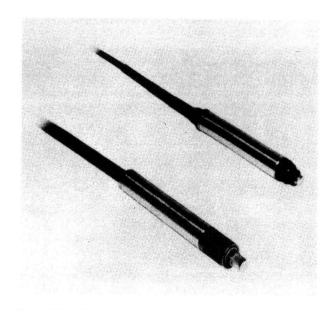

Fig. 7-19   Cartridge-type electronic gage heads. (Courtesy of Federal Products Corporation)

LVDT and E-Transformer Transducers

Many electronic gaging systems use a linear-variable-differential-transformer (LVDT) as the detector/transducer element in the gage head. An LVDT is an electromechanical transducer that converts physical motion into an output voltage whose amplitude and phase are proportional to the displacement of a separate movable core. It consists of one primary and two secondary coils equally spaced around a common cylindrical core that is an extension of the spindle (as shown in Fig. 7-20). The cylindrical magnetic core, positioned axially inside the coil assembly, provides a path for the magnetic flux linking the coils. When an AC voltage is applied to the primary coil, a voltage is induced in the two secondary coils. The secondary coils are connected in series opposition, so that the two voltages in the secondary circuit are opposite in phase. Thus, the net output of the transformer is the *difference* between the voltages of the two secondary windings. When the core is positioned approximately in the center of the transformer, the output voltage is zero. This is called the *balance point* or *null position.*

When the core is moved from the null position toward the first secondary coil, the voltage induced in that secondary coil increases, whereas—simul-

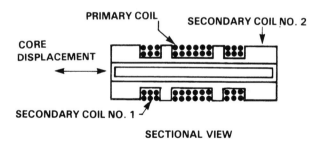

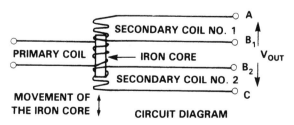

Fig. 7-20   Sectional view of a linear-variable-differential-transformer (LVDT) and schematic diagram.

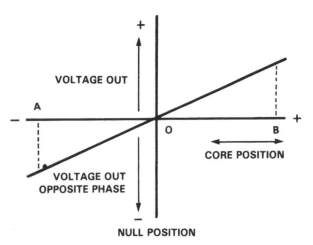

Fig. 7-21   Output voltage as a function of core position of a linear-variable-differential-transformer (LVDT).

taneously—the voltage induced in the other secondary coil decreases. This produces a differential voltage output that varies linearly with the change in core position. Motion of the core from the null position in the opposite direction produces a similar linear voltage characteristic with the phase shifted 180 deg. A continuous plot of voltage output versus core position (see Fig. 7-21), using opposite algebraic signs to indicate opposite phases, appears as a straight line through the origin.

Some electronic gaging systems use the E-transformer instead of the LVDT in the gaging head. The E-transformer (sometimes called a

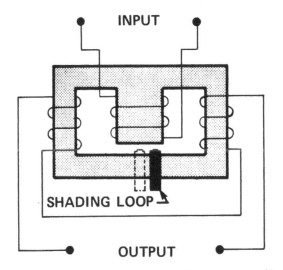

Fig. 7-22   Schematic diagram of an E-transformer. (Courtesy of Federal Products Corporation)

shading loop) is very similar to the LVDT, except that the coils are wound around a laminated iron core in the shape of the letter E, with the primary and secondary coils wound around the center and outside legs as shown in Fig. 7-22. The magnetic path is completed through an armature whose linear motion varies the induced voltage in the secondary coils, as in the LVDT. The E-transformer, like the LVDT, is sensitive to extremely small motions.

Electronic Gaging Systems

Unlike the electric gage, which produces a digital output, the electronic gage head produces a continuous analog output which is usually amplified and presented on a moving coil meter, numerical display board or recorder, or a combination of these devices. Like the electric gage, the electronic gage head provides switching points, but the switching is accomplished electronically rather than mechanically. Although the electronic gage is more complex than the electric gage, the use of solid-state circuitry makes the gage very reliable.

In addition to producing high magnifications, electronic gaging systems provide a choice of magnifications by means of switch selection. This allows the gage or comparator to be used over a wide range of tolerance measurements, and facilitates preliminary adjustment in situations where final measurement is made at high magnification levels. Some systems incorporate electrical zero adjustment having a range many times that of the operating range, thereby eliminating the need for critical positoning of the gage head.

In operation, alternating voltage is brought to the gage head where it is altered by movement of the mechanical spindle, directly or indirectly, as it responds to the size of the workpiece.

The voltage output is fed through several stages of transistor amplification, rectified (changed from ac to dc), and impressed upon a suitable voltmeter that has linear graduations in terms of workpiece size. Because the speed of response is practically instantaneous, the electronic gage is especially suited to high-speed gaging, sorting, and classifying in automatic gaging machines, and ultra-precise laboratory measuring applications.

One electronic gaging system that employs an LVDT is shown in Fig. 7-23. The core, attached

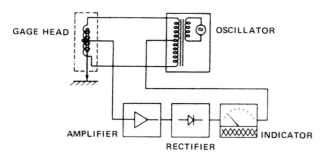

Fig. 7-23   Impedance-type gaging system with LVDT. (Courtesy of Brown & Sharpe Manufacturing Company)

to the gage spindle, moves axially and its position in relation to the coils affects the impedance of the coils. The coils and a symmetrical transformer in the oscillator form a bridge. When the core rests equally between the two coils, the bridge is balanced and the output signal from the gage head is zero. When the core is displaced, the impedance of the coils is changed. The impedance of one coil is reduced while that of the other coil is increased, which generates a signal in proportion to the amount of displacement of the core. The signal is then amplified, rectified, and indicated on a dc

meter calibrated in units of length. Differential amplifiers can be used with two gage heads simultaneously in this system to determine the difference between, or the sum of, two measurements. Typical applications of such a differential gaging system (see Fig. 7-24) include checking: roundness, concentricity, parallelism, thickness, cam contours, tapers, flatness, and squareness—without precision fixturing.

In Fig. 7-24A, when two gage heads are placed parallel and on the same side of a workpiece and master with properly-actuated settings, the indicator will show the difference between them. If both the master and the workpiece are affected by the same source of error D (such as temperature), the difference will remain the same. This type of setup can be used for measuring roundness, parallelism, and flatness.

In Fig. 7-24B, only the difference in concentricity will show on the indicator. If both parts are out-of-round in the same amount, the reading will not be affected.

By placing two gage heads parallel on a tapered part, as shown in Fig. 7-24C, you can check the degree of taper as compared with a master part,

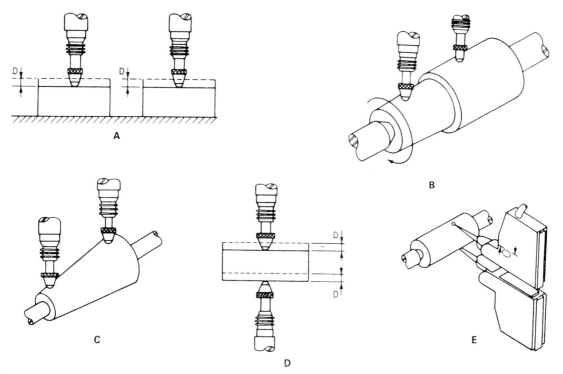

Fig. 7-24   Typical applications of differential gaging.   (Courtesy of Brown & Sharpe Manufacturing Company)

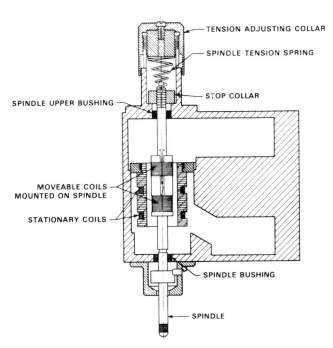

Fig. 7-25   Movable coil gage head. (Courtesy of Federal Products Corporation)

without regard to its diameter.

By placing two gage heads perpendicular and opposite to the workpiece with properly-actuated gage settings, as shown in Fig. 7-24D, the indicator will show the sum of the two D errors. This means that, if the workpiece is displaced either upward or downward, the indicator reading will not change. The top gage head will move a distance of $+D$, while the bottom gage head will move a distance of $-D$. Because they will cancel each other out, the reading of the thickness of the part will not change. This type of setup can be used to measure thickness or diameter without requiring precision fixtures.

Using the setup shown in Fig. 7-24E, the diameter of a workpiece can be compared with that of a master without precision fixtures. The reason is that neither upward nor downward displacement will affect the accuracy of the reading.

The differential gaging technique is well suited to selecting parts having a specific clearance but whose actual size is not critical; for example, in mating the ID of a cylinder with the OD of a piston.

Another electronic gaging system that employs an LDVT is shown in Fig. 7-25. As the core changes position in relation to the two stationary secondary coils in the gage head, they induce a greater or lesser voltage in direct proportion to the spindle displacement, displacing the indicating hand on the meter accordingly. The change is amplified to a usable quantity, achieving magnifications as high as 100,000:1.

An electronic plug gaging system is shown in Fig. 7-26, which uses a cartridge-type gage head and combines the great accuracy of solid state circuitry with the ease and speed of plug gaging. Because amplification of the signal is linear instead of point-to-point, the electronic plug gage requires only a single master ring for setting instead of both the minimum and maximum setting masters used in pneumatic plug gaging systems. In operation, the electronic gaging plug is simply inserted into a bore, and its deviation from zero is read on the meter scale. No "rocking" of the gage head is required to locate the true diameter.

In the electronic plug gaging system, both the size of the gaging plugs and the amplifier range modules can be changed from job to job, permitting a single amplifier and handle assembly to be used for many different bore gaging applications. Gaging plugs are available in two different styles for thru-holes and blind holes in five gaging ranges for sizes from 0.250 in. (6.35mm) to 4.500 in. (114.3mm), and extensions can be furnished for

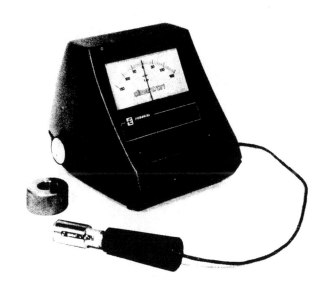

Fig. 7-26   Electronic plug gaging system. (Courtesy of Federal Products Corporation)

certain sizes to allow gaging at depths up to 7.78 in. (200mm). Each plug is designed to check a specific diameter, and is marked with its size and gaging range. Because both of the opposed gaging contacts are sensitive, the plug can also check other bore conditions, such as ovality, barrel shape, bell mouth, and taper. A bench stand allows the gaging plugs to be mounted in a stationary position for use in comparison measurements.

The electronic plug gaging system has five different models of amplifiers: three in the inch ranges and two in the metric ranges. Interchangeable magnification kits convert one model to any of the other gaging ranges so that amplifier magnification can be changed to suit different workpiece tolerances. Each kit consists of a meter scale and a plug-in amplifier range module.

SURFACE TEXTURE MEASURING

Surface finish for parts is specified with greater frequency today in industry. As moving parts are designed to encounter higher loadings and increased speeds, high quality finishes become critical to the functioning of parts. All machined surfaces consist of a series of peaks and valleys which when magnified resemble the surface of a phonograph record. The characteristics of surface texture, or finish, are roughness, waviness, lay and flaw (Fig. 7-27). Surface roughness is the finely spaced surface irregularity usually caused by the cutting action of the tool edges, the cutting pattern of a grinding wheel or by the speed and feed of the machine tool, as measured over a specific distance. It is measured in microinches (0.000001 in.). Waviness, measured in inches, is similar to rough-

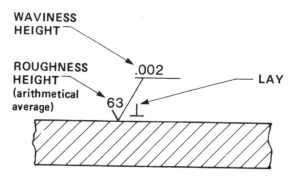

Fig. 7-29   Surface texture symbol.

ness but it occurs over a wider spacing than that used for determining roughness. Roughness may be considered as superimposed on a "wavy" surface. Lay indicates the direction of the predominant surface pattern with symbols as shown in Fig. 7-28. Flaws are irregularities, or defects, which

Fig. 7-30   Surfanalyzer® System—Precision surface analyzing system. (Courtesy of Federal Products Corporation)

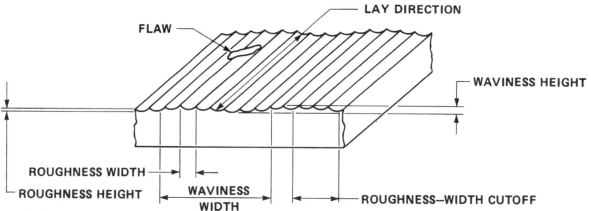

Fig. 7-27   Surface texture characteristics.

occur at one place, or relatively infrequently in a surface, but are usually used as the reference area for measuring surface texture. Fig. 7-29 illustrates the surface symbol specified on an engineering drawing.

The two principle reasons surface finish controls are specified on engineering drawings are to reduce friction and to control wear. Overfinishing and underfinishing the job adds unnecessarily to the production cost and can result in the rejection of a part or an entire production run. Surface texture measurement calls for the use of precise measuring equipment and is covered by American National Standards Institute, ANS B46.1-1978 Surface Texture.

Surface finish or texture measurements can be made with reasonable accuracy by scratching the surface being tested with your fingernail and comparing the relative roughness against a microfinish comparator. The microfinish comparator is a

LAY SYMBOL	DESIGNATION	EXAMPLE
‖	Lay parallel to the line representing the surface to which the symbol is applied. 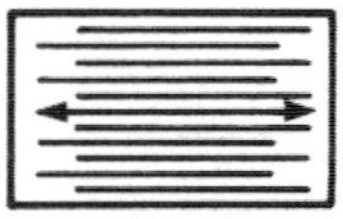 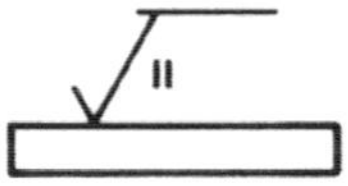	
⊥	Lay perpendicular to the line representing the surface to which the symbol is applied. 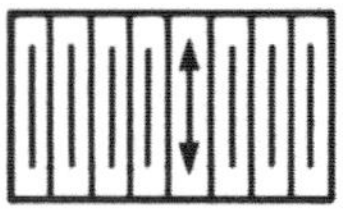 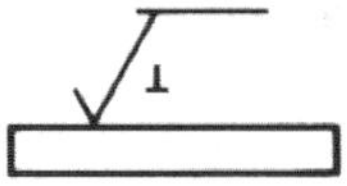	
X	Lay angular in both directions to line representing the surface to which symbol is applied.  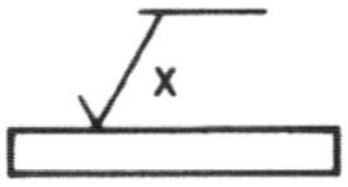	
M	Lay multidirectional 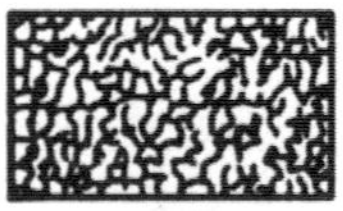 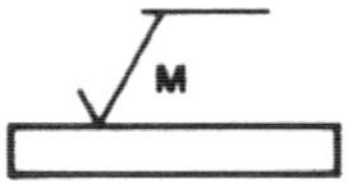	
C	Lay approximately circular relative to the center of the surface to which the symbol is applied.  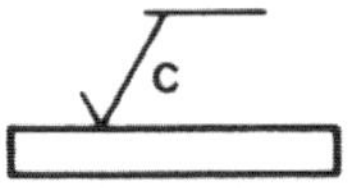	
R	Lay approximately radial relative to the center of the surface to which the symbol is applied.  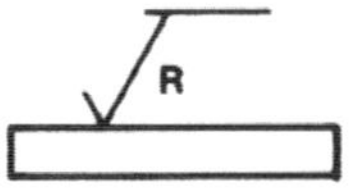	

Fig. 7-28   Lay symbols.

simple scale that contains a number of surface specimens where the roughness of each is identified. The accuracy of the scratch test is totally dependent upon the skill and feel factors of the tester.

Precision linear surface measurement is done with electronic test equipment systems. The Surfanalyzer® System shown in Fig. 7-30 can measure, compute, display and record the linear profile and surface finish characteristics. This system consists of a control center with a recorder, a precision linear drive mechanism and a probe. As the linear drive moves across the test area, the probe measures the surface characteristics in microinches (or micrometers) which are then analyzed, displayed and/or recorded through the control center.

OPTICAL COMPARATORS

The optical comparator (also called *optical projector* and *contour projector*) is used to measure many kinds of parts that are—because of size, material composition, or dimensional characteristics—difficult to measure with other methods. All optical comparators operate fundamentally alike:

They all display magnified images on an appropriate viewing screen as an aid to making more precise determinations of dimension, form, and sometimes physical characteristics of parts. The images must be clear, sharp, and dimensionally accurate. Therefore, the mechanical design and operation of the projector must also be compatible with the precision of the optical system.

The special advantage of optical comparators is that they can display a two-dimensional projection of a part, rather than a single linear dimension as do most other gaging systems.

System Components

Optical measuring and gaging systems include certain essential elements:

(1) Light source,

(2) Condenser or collimating lens system to direct light past the part and into the optical system,

(3) Workpiece staging table,

(4) Projection optics (including both mirrors and lenses),

(5) Viewing screen, and

(6) Measuring devices (where required).

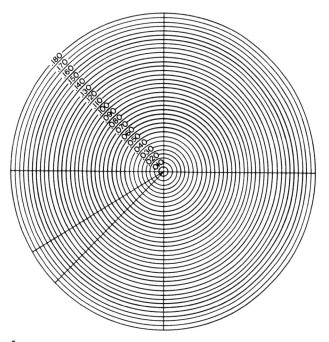

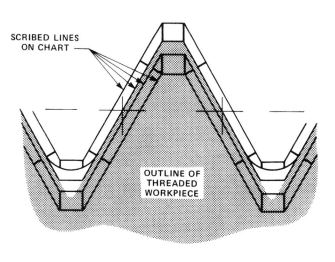

A

B

Fig. 7-31   Standard chart gage (A) and tolerance outline chart for a screw thread (B). (Courtesy of DoAll Company)

The arrangement of these elements varies in different comparators, but their function is the same in each. A part is measured or gaged by placing it in the path of a beam of light in front of a magnifying lens system, which projects an enlarged silhouette of the part onto a translucent receiving (viewing) screen. In measuring applications, a chart gage (see Fig. 7-31) is required having reference lines in two dimensions. In gaging applications, a precisely scaled layout of the contour of the part to be gaged—usually containing tolerance limits—is drawn on the receiving screen, as shown in Fig. 7-32.

In its simplest form, an optical comparator is constructed according to the schematic diagram shown in Fig. 7-33. Figure 7-34 shows a high precision optical comparator. Such a system can be used both in inspection and for making comparison measurements. In machine shop applications and for single-piece inspections, a comparator must have precision in its staging table mechanism and in the measuring devices associated with it. Because measurements are made with reference to a crossline in the center of the projector screen, the image does not have to be completely accurate over the entire screen. However, when a comparator is used to make comparison measurements, the projected part image is compared with an enlarged layout placed directly on the screen, and may be spread over the entire screen area. In these applications, accuracy of the image in *all* areas of the screen is very important. Since in most industrial plants, comparators are frequently used for both applications, optical comparator equipment must have both a

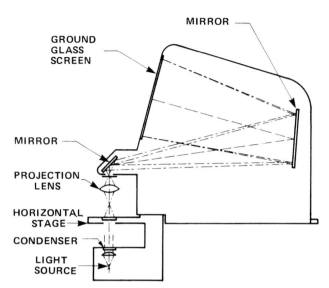

Fig. 7-33 *Schematic arrangement of elements of direct-light optical comparator. (Courtesy of DoAll Company)*

precise optical system, and a means for precise mechanical measuring.

Projector Light Sources. In all optical comparators, a beam of light is the medium that actually presents a measurable image of a test part on the viewing screen for examination. Three arrangements of light sources are used in optical comparators: horizontal, vertical, and surface. Both horizontal and vertical systems are designed to produce a shadow image on the screen. Surface illumination, as its name implies, produces a reflected image of the surface of a part. Most comparators employ a single type of shadow projection, although some designs incorporate both horizontal and vertical systems in the same unit. Surface illumination is usually considered optional equipment on a comparator, and may be mounted externally or internally.

Comparators equipped with horizontal beams are used widely in industry. Their basic arrangement permits them to have a large open staging area. In vertical light systems, the light source may be located above the work area or below it. A mirror is inserted into the path of the vertical beam after it passes the workpiece to direct it into the projection system. Thus, the staging areas used with vertical systems incorporate a glass plate or cutout for the passage of the light beam, on which workpieces can be placed for inspection.

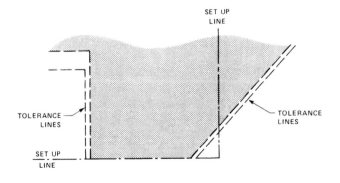

Fig. 7-32 *Optical gaging for tolerance. (Courtesy of DoAll Company)*

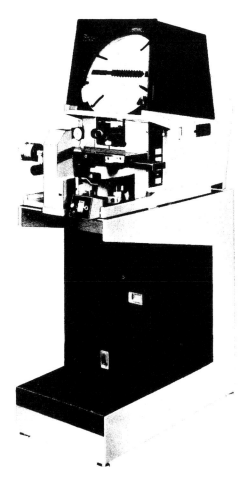

Fig. 7-34   High precision optical comparator. (Courtesy of DoAll Company)

The light sources most generally used are tungsten filament lamps and high-pressure mercury or xenon arc lamps. The ideal projector lamp would be one that is capable of producing a concentrated bundle of parallel light rays (or beams) of sufficient diameter to illuminate a significant area of a part for projection. Because no such lamp exists, an approximation of this ideal is achieved by optical means wherein an achromatic collimator lens system is placed in the path of the beam as it leaves the lamp. The lens collects sufficient light rays into a parallel beam of large enough diameter to provide both coverage of the part and adequate illumination intensity at the screen. However, collimation can collect only a limited number of the total light rays emitted by the lamp, and a continual loss of light occurs within the beam itself as it passes through the optical system, due to scattering, reflection from lens and mirror surfaces, and absorption within the system.

When it is necessary to have greatly intensified illumination to project non-reflective materials, irregular surfaces, or extremely small components at very high magnifications, the high-pressure mercury or xenon arc lamps are used, which have great intensity. These light sources are very effective in producing good contrast between shadow image and background light for comparative purposes.

Surface Illumination — The light sources used to illuminate the surface of the part to be measured differ from the two projector light sources described above. To project surface characteristics effectively, the light sources used must be more intense than those used for direct projection. These surface illumination assemblies are generally accessory equipment added to the exterior of a comparator. The light beam is first directed onto the part surface by mirrors, and then reflected back into the normal projection system of the projector. In projectors where the surface illumination system is incorporated as an integral part of the projector, the beam reflects directly from the part back into the projection system. High-intensity sources that converge available light in a concentrated beam on a part make possible the projection of such dull and non-reflective materials as ceramic and carbon.

Staging Areas

The most important part of an optical system used for inspection is the staging or work area. The work table supports the workpiece to be examined, and holds it in the light beam from the collimator. Work tables may be stationary or moving. Stationary tables are equipped with keyways and/or T-slots to provide a surface for mounting fixtures.

Moving tables usually have provision for the attachment of measuring devices. Many are equipped with an angular adjustment for positioning to the helix of threads and worms. Protractor rings mounted with the viewing screen simplify the determination of angular measurements.

Moving tables generally provide travel in three planes: focus, horizontal, and vertical. On a comparator with a horizontal beam, the focus travel is an in-and-out movement parallel to the axis of the light beam. The table usually moves on friction or ball slides, and is controlled by a handwheel or knob.

The focusing movement on a vertical beam comparator must be vertical. In these comparators, the tables are usually mounted on dovetail or box-type slides that are rigidly aligned and controlled. To permit the passage of the light beam, the table has a flat glass surface set into the top, which allows a variety of flat parts to be positioned without any other special fixturing. The remainder of the table top may be fitted with standard keyway slots for mounting centers or other fixtures to hold parts over the glass in the light path.

Projection Systems

After the light beam passes the workpiece, it passes into the projection system consisting of lenses and mirrors held in accurate alignment on rigid supports. The lenses provide the desired magnification, whereas the mirrors both direct the light beam to the viewing screen, and help to form an image on the screen in the same orientation as the operator sees the workpiece in the staging area. Interchangeable lenses allow selection of the magnification best suited to the requirements of the operation. In some projectors, the lenses must be changed manually, whereas in others, several lenses are mounted in a turret or slide. An external control allows the operator to index the turret to bring the desired lens into the projection system.

Low-power magnification has certain advantages over high-power magnification in both inspection and comparison measurement applications. Low-power magnification projects images on the screen that are sharply delineated with clean-cut edges, and have a positive contrast between shadow and background light that greatly simplifies making settings to reference lines on the screen. In addition, for comparison measurements, low-power magnification projects a larger portion of the workpiece at a single setting.

The most frequently used lens magnifications are 10:1, 20:1, 25:1, 50:1, and 100:1, all of which provide a multiple of the unit increment of 0.001 in. Some very high-power lenses provide magnifications ranging from 200:1 to 2500:1. They are

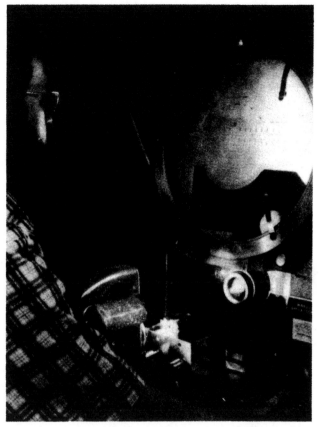

Fig. 7-35   In this view, the light source, staging area and viewing screen are clearly visible as the operator measures the radius of a ground part.

used mainly in comparison measurement applications.

Viewing Screens

After passing through the projection lens, the light beam is directed by mirrors to the viewing screen where the image of the workpiece is formed. Viewing screens are made from glass with one surface ground to a very fine grain. The ground surface of the screen must be perfectly flat. Any waviness can cause distortion of an image in different portions of the screen. (See Fig. 7-35.)

Basic Measurement Techniques

The three basic techniques used for measurement with optical comparators are: (1) measurement by comparison, (2) measurement by movement, and (3) measurement by translation.

The inspections performed on many parts are essentially GO, NOT-GO inspections made by comparison to a master. All optical comparators can, within the capability of their optical and mechanical design, make measurements by comparison. However, to measure by movement requires a comparator equipped with table travel and appropriate measuring devices. Measurement by translation, or indirect measurement of contours, requires special tracer accessories.

Measurement by Comparison. The two-dimensional images produced by optical comparators provide the means for making measurements by comparison. These images magnify the dimensions of parts positioned in the focal plane of the optical system exactly. Thus, a master layout or chart-gage can be made to represent the high and low limits of the theoretically perfect part at the magnified size, and then be compared to the screen image. If the image falls within the limits of the master gage, the part is acceptable. If it does not, the part is a reject.

Chart-gages are generally of the envelope type in which dimensions and tolerances are interpreted so as to produce a double-line outline that delineates the allowable maximum and minimum conditions of the part. A reference line is included for alignment of the part image to the chart. Chart-gages can also show all of the contour characteristics of a part, such as irregular curves, chamfers, and fillet radii. For more critical dimensions, scales or close tolerance line construction is added to enhance readability.

A holding device or staging fixture is generally used with a chart-gage when performing inspections by comparison. The staging fixture supports the part so that the area or contour to be projected is positioned in the focal plane of the optical system. In many cases, the same holding device can support a number of different parts, such as sets of matched staging centers and V-blocks whose bases are designed to fit the table keyways.

Measurement by Movement. Measurement by movement is used primarily for single-piece inspection, or for making several non-repetitive measurements. This technique relates the travel of the work table to a positive index or reference. The optical axis of the comparator serves as an appropriate reference, and is identified by the center crossline on the screen. The vertical crossline is referenced when using horizontal table travel, and the horizontal crossline is referenced when moving the screen image up or down. In most comparators, table movement to the left or right causes the screen image to also move horizontally. Table movement that produces a vertical shifting of the image varies according to how the light beam is directed. On horizontal beam comparators, vertical movement of the image is produced by raising or lowering the work table. If the comparator has a vertical beam, the image shifts vertically as the work table is moved to and from the operator standing in front of the screen.

Measurement by Translation. Many parts can be gaged on optical projectors, even though their configurations cannot be projected by the light beam. For example, parts having recessed contours (such as actuator cam tracks, ball sockets, and the internal grooves of ball nuts) can all be gaged by

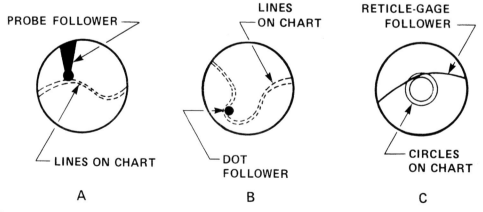

Fig. 7-36   Tracer followers: probe type (A), dot type (B), and reticle-gage type (C).

means of tracer techniques. The term *tracer*, used in projection gaging, is a one-to-one pantograph. On one arm of the pantograph, a stylus traces freely over the part contour in a given plane. The other arm carries a follower which is projected by the light beam as it moves. Three types of followers are used, as shown in Fig. 7-36.

(1) *Probe follower* (A)—an exact duplicate of the stylus tracer in size and shape.

(2) *Dot follower* (B)—a glass reticle having an opaque dot of the same diameter as the stylus tracer.

(3) *Reticle-gage follower* (C)—a glass reticle having an exact one-to-one size reproduction of the part profile.

Which follower to use in a given gaging problem depends upon the size of the part and the magnification required. In general, the probe or dot is used if the size of the part is less than the field of view of the projector at the given magnification. Some larger parts can be gaged by using two followers suitably spaced to correlate with a special type of chart-gage in which one section of the contour is superimposed on another section. Sometimes the dot follower is better than the probe, because it provides a complete circle shadow unrestricted by the shadow of the supporting stem.

The reticle-gage follower is more versatile in its application, because it is unrestricted by part size or magnification. This type of follower allows very large parts to be gaged, using high magnification. Reticle-gages must be very accurate, because any inherent error shows up as an error in the part.

Tracer units equipped with either probe or dot followers are used with chart-gages showing a contour layout of the part. The layout may be either a single-line or double-line profile showing the permissible limits of the part. As the stylus traces across the part, the projected image of the follower moves across the screen. If a single-line chart is used, the follower shadow must remain tangent to the line throughout the transit for a part to be without error. Using a double-line chart, the edge of the follower shadow must always remain between the two lines.

A different type of chart-gage is used when tracing with a reticle-gage follower (see Fig. 7-31A). This chart has a circle on it representing the diameter of the stylus tracer at the magnification being used. The projected reticle-gage contour moves past this fixed circle as the part is traced and, if the part is perfect, remains tangent to it. If the tolerance limits on the part are uniform throughout, two circles can be used on the screen to represent the tolerance spread. The projected reticle contour should then fall between the two circles as it passes across the screen. If the part tolerance varies from point to point along the contour, the tolerance lines can be used on the reticle follower, and projected to a single circle on the screen.

Standard tracer units with coordinate slides are available as accessory equipment for most comparators. They can be fitted with special stylus arms for specific purposes, such as tracing internal contours and checking for concentricity. Some tracers are designed for use with horizontal light beams, others are designed for use with a vertical beam.

MEASURING MACHINES

There is no precise or all-inclusive definition of a measuring machine, but the name is used to designate different types of machines that are used to perform one or more of the following inspection functions:

(1) External and internal measurements of lengths and diameters,

(2) External and internal tapers,

(3) Angular measurement and circular division,

(4) Coordinate measurement of points, holes, and surfaces, and

(5) External and internal thread measurement.

Most inspection processes in the shop yield values of error rather than simply accepting or rejecting parts. Thus, the major portion of the time required for such inspection is used in taking measurements, especially open setup inspection on a surface plate. Measuring machines were developed to speed up the taking of measurements for an inspection, and to reduce the potential for errors. Measuring machines are distinguished from comparators by allowing a larger range of measurement and incorporating their own standard of measurement in the form of a leadscrew, micrometer, precision scale, or other integral system. They are designed for work requiring a high degree of accuracy.

Three principal types of measuring machines are the single-axis universal, multiple-axis universal, and coordinate.

SINGLE-AXIS UNIVERSAL MEASURING MACHINE

An example of a single-axis universal measuring machine is shown in Fig. 7-37. This machine can be used to measure length, diameter, pitch diameter, roundness, straightness, parallelism, and taper. It can measure long parts up to the length limit of the machine, which is 80 in. on the standard model, although other lengths are available.

Measuring Principle

The machine operates by combining the functions of two master standards: a measuring bar and a precision dividing screw. The measurements taken on this machine can be read directly to 0.00001 in. or 0.0002mm.

The single-axis universal measuring machine

Fig. 7-37   Single-axis universal measuring machine. (Courtesy of Pratt & Whitney Machine Tool Division, Measuring Systems Operation)

shown in Fig. 7-37 consists basically of a mounting bed and ways upon which the measuring head and tailstock move. The primary measuring standard of the machine is the master bar, located at the rear of the mounting bed. The master bar has lapped stainless steel measuring buttons located at 1 in. (or 25mm if the bar is metric) intervals. At the exact location of each inch (or 25mm), a hairline is inscribed on the buttons to serve as reference points. The exact separation of 1 in. or 25mm has been transferred, under special control and clean-room conditions, from a master bar calibrated at the National Bureau of Standards in Washington, DC.

The measuring head contains the dividing screw, a microscope, and a zeroing milliammeter. The dividing screw, which precisely moves the spindle longitudinally to the measuring position divides the inch into 0.00001 increments. A vernier dial, attached to the dividing screw, gives direct measuring readouts to 0.0001 in. when the milliammeter—activated by a transducer in the tailstock—indicates a centered needle. The 75-power microscope allows accurate alignment of the measuring head at the desired reference points on the master bar.

The tailstock (a patented feature of this particular machine), provides consistent measuring pressures—adjustable from 2 to 48 oz—so that identical readings can be taken by different operators, thereby eliminating the introduction of any error caused by improper "feel." These pressures are displayed on the milliammeter in the measuring head. The basic circuitry in the tailstock consists of a transducer that produces a signal proportional to the displacement of the gaging anvil, which is amplified to activate the milliammeter in the measuring head. The tailstock transducer contains two inductances between which an armature is mounted on steel reeds. A displacement of the gaging anvil moves the armature, which unbalances a bridge circuit to move the milliammeter.

The light gaging pressure control tailstock is designed primarily for taking measurements on parts where microfinish and type or hardness of material influence the gaging pressures required. It also meets the pressure requirements for measuring thread gages, and for gaging small, light, thin parts, such as those used in miniaturization.

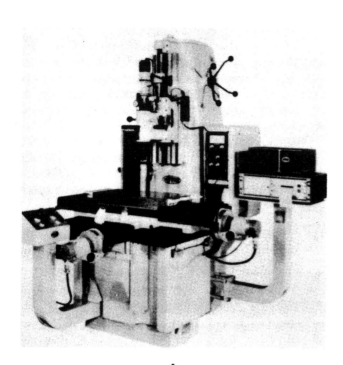

A

MULTIPLE-AXIS UNIVERSAL MEASURING MACHINE

Whereas the single-axis universal measuring machine is a precision *linear* measuring instrument, the multiple-axis universal measuring machines shown in Fig. 7-38 are capable of analyzing *both linear and geometric* dimensions of: distance, roundness, straightness, and perpendicularity of surfaces in all planes; and the magnitude of angles when a circle-dividing device is added to the system.

The four basic features for universal application that these measuring machines incorporate are defined as control of: geometry, length, angles, and roundness. The relationship of all features of a workpiece can be determined, because the slides, measuring system, and spindle of these universal measuring machines are integrated into a single work center. This is accomplished by combining:

(1) A linear measuring system of great accuracy having three axes of motion with precise 90 deg relationships to each other (see Fig. 7-39),

(2) A rotatable spindle with trueness of rotation of less than 0.000005 in. total indicator reading (TIR), and

(3) Angular measuring accessories having an accuracy of ±0.1 second of arc.

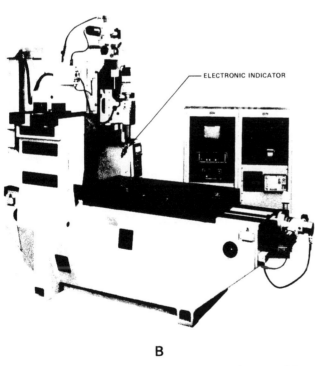

— ELECTRONIC INDICATOR

B

Fig. 7-38   Multiple-axis universal measuring machines. (Courtesy of Moore Special Tool Company, Inc.)

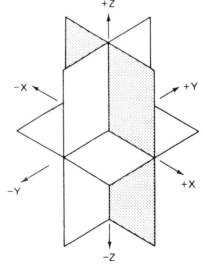

Fig. 7-39   Conventional cartesian coordinate system showing linear motion along and about each of the three axes of machine tool motion: X, Y, and Z.

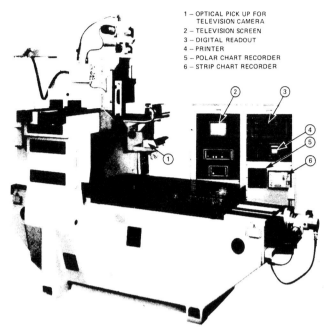

1 – OPTICAL PICK UP FOR
    TELEVISION CAMERA
2 – TELEVISION SCREEN
3 – DIGITAL READOUT
4 – PRINTER
5 – POLAR CHART RECORDER
6 – STRIP CHART RECORDER

Fig. 7-40   This multiple-axis universal measuring machine is equipped with: (1) optical pickup for television camera, (2) television screen, (3) digital readout, (4) printer, (5) polar chart recorder, and (6) strip chart recorder. (Courtesy of Moore Special Tool Company, Inc.)

The machines' spindle axis of rotation serves as the zero point that describes a line parallel to the Z axis. This provides the point of origin for all measurements in the X-Y plane. The precision spindle rotates to establish bore centerline location, and runs true. The accuracy of the spindle's rotation is less than 0.000005 in. (0.00012mm) TIR. This means that its axis of rotation will not deviate from absolute zero more than this amount, thereby assuring the certainty of its position.

The adjustable gage head with its probe can describe precise circles that are infinitely variable in size. This circular motion, combined with the precise straightline vertical adjustment of the spindle assembly, provides the means for inspecting complete cylindrical forms. A motor drive with slip-ring coupling for the indicator—whose speed of rotation is synchronized with a polar recorder—allow measuring and recording of roundness geometry. Both cylindrical and concentric characteristics of the workpiece are graphically represented on a circular chart.

When the slide motions are employed directly, the straightness and parallelism of related surfaces can be measured by directly comparing the workpiece surfaces to the precise straightline travel of the machine slide. The measurements are recorded on a linear recording chart.

Programable positioning control systems can be used to position the slide coordinates to the part specification. If this procedure is followed, deviations from nominal can be evaluated by three types of pickup systems:

(1) Conventional electronic indicators showing amplified readings of the part deviation on a dial or recording chart,

(2) A microscope viewing the workpiece detail visually or electronically, and

(3) Magnified optical projection of the detail through either a system of lenses, or by means of a closed-circuit television camera and screen.

The appropriate pickup system then relates the workpiece dimensional features to the universal measuring machine's coordinate measuring system. Deviations can be evaluated by comparing the actual dimensions to the engineering specification.

An alternate method is to position the machine to specified workpiece dimensions, and either note or record the deviation indicated by the pickup system.

When a universal measuring machine is equipped with a contouring N/C system capable of generating precise contouring motions, it can be used as an infinitely variable master contour generator. Any form that can be generated by the synchronously-controlled motion of the machine's linear slides can be evaluated by direct comparison to the controlled motion. A pickup device, such as an electronic indicator, is used to monitor surface deviation. Because the full capacity of the measuring machine can be employed in measuring the workpiece, contoured surfaces up to 24 in. x 48 in. (600mm x 1200mm) can be measured to parts-of-a-tenth accuracy. The entire part profile can be examined in a continuous contouring mode, and deviations recorded on a strip chart.

Fig. 7-41   Coordinate measuring machine. (Courtesy of
Bendix Automation & Measurement Division)

COORDINATE MEASURING MACHINES

Coordinate measuring machines operate on a different principle from either the single-axis or multiple-axis universal measuring machines. Coordinate measuring machines (CMMs) are displacement measuring devices consisting basically of a staging table and a travelling member or gage head with a mounted sensing probe. The measuring system first senses the separation between the individual points of reference (the boundary points) on a part held on the staging table in discrete increments of a unit of measure (inch or metric). The length of the sensed displacement is then displayed in digital form. Most CMMs are equipped with staging tables that accommodate a wide range of part sizes, as shown in Fig. 7-41.

The travelling member is guided along two straightline paths contained in a common plane that are mutually perpendicular and that represent the X and Y axes of a rectangular system of coordinates. In some CMMs, probe travel includes a third axis—the Z axis with a direction normal to the plane of the X and Y axes—for vertical measurements. The guideways of the travelling head are of two basic types: bridge-type (vertical arm) or cantilever (horizontal arm). The guide-

ways permit an almost frictionless displacement of the gage head by applying a very small force. Contact probes in various forms and sizes are used to locate the boundary points of the distances being measured on the part.

Coordinate measuring machines have developed to their present level of sophistication from early modifications of precision layout machines made in the late 1950s. They were developed primarily to provide faster first-piece inspection and/or 100% inspection of parts produced on numerically-controlled (N/C) machine tools. It is said that CMMs revolutionized quality control procedures in production by considerably speeding up traditional inspection methods using surface plates, angle irons, gage blocks, etc. The traditional methods sometimes require more time to inspect a part than it takes to make it. In addition, data collected by a CMM during inspection of the total work cycle can indicate variations in both the machine and the operator, as well as provide feedback information to manufacturing that permits the correction of production errors without having to throw away parts.

CMMs are often compared to N/C machine tools, because they both operate on numerical data plotted on coordinate axes. On an N/C machine, numerical data fed into the control directs the machine tool to cut a certain configuration. On a CMM, a probe moves in and out of holes around the part while the numerical data displayed by the machine determines whether the part meets the specifications on the drawing. Thus, CMMs inspect parts in much the same way that N/C machines make them. CMMs are suited to applications ranging from one-of-a-kind, first-part inspections to short and medium production runs. Various styles of CMMs operate under manual, motorized, or numerical control. The mode of measurement may be direct, by deviation, or by a combination of these two methods. Direct measuring machines with digital readout are the most commonly used. They provide direct or absolute measurement of probe position or movement in three axes to 0.001 or 0.000050 in. resolution.

Direct Computer Control (DCC) is the abbreviated term used to define a CMM that is completely driven by computer programs. This means that part programs written in a computer language drive the machine's axes and inspect a part

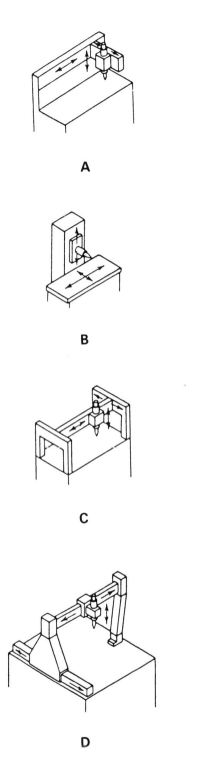

A

B

C

D

Fig. 7-42   Four typical design configurations of coordinate measuring machines: (A) back wall cantilever, (B) horizontal spindle, (C) travelling bridge, and (D) overhead bridge or gantry.

automatically.

A CMM that operates under DCC has servo-drive motors on each axis that can be used to position the probe during an inspection. During the initial setup procedure, some probes can be either manually moved or motor driven under "joy stick" control by the operator. Once the reference points of the part have been located, the computer program takes over, automatically inspecting the part and issuing the inspection report.

Computer-directed displays can display part or machine coordinates directly in either polar or cartesian coordinates, together with various other computed program or part variables, such as diameters, deviations, out-of-tolerances in inch or metric, time of day, etc.

The data handling capability of a CMM was significantly increased by the addition of computers, microprocessors, and calculators. The computer-assisted CMMs provide automatic part alignment, general-purpose programs, and much faster calculating capability than could be performed by an operator or inspector. These systems store part programs on paper tape or magnetic or floppy disks for future use in inspecting similar parts. No operator intervantion is required in the routines.

General-purpose programs of the subroutines required to perform a particular inspection task (such as taking a three-point reading or displaying the actual readings in the X and Y axes) are stored in the integral measurement preprocessing system. In addition, a specific program can be configured interactively by an operator for a particular part being inspected, such as a circle of bolt holes. By selecting the proper combination of the general-purpose routines, an operator can build a complete program to totally inspect a part. This capability is particularly useful when inspecting many one-of-a-kind parts for which the writing of a detailed program is not economical in cost or time.

MEASURING HARDNESS

Materials are measured for hardness by comparison with other materials. Hardness measurement is a relative characteristic, unlike roughness which has a measurable physical dimension. The machinist considers hardness as an index of the machinability of a material. A metallurgist, how-

Scale	Penetrator	Major Load (kg)	Testing Application
A	Brale	60	For tungsten carbide and other extremely hard materials. Also for thin, hard sheets.
B	$1/16$ in. ball	100	For materials of medium hardness such as low and medium carbon steels in the annealed condition.
C	Brale	150	For materials harder than Rockwell B-100.
D	Brale	100	Where somewhat lighter load is desired than on C scale, as on case hardened pieces.
E	$1/8$ in. ball	100	For very soft materials such as bearing metals.
F	$1/16$ in. ball	60	Same as E scale but using $1/16$-inch ball.
G	$1/16$ in. ball	150	For metals harder than tested on B scale.

Fig. 7-43   Rockwell hardness testing — standards and applications.

ever, relates hardness to the wear characteristics and to the ability of the material to resist indententation or penetration.

Mechanical methods to test hardness measure the resistance the material offers to penetration by an even harder standard penetrator, such as a $1/16$ in. steel ball or a diamond cone called a Brale. A preset load or force presses the penetrator into the surface being tested. A number representative of the relative hardness is obtained by measuring or comparing the indentation made by the penetrator in the test piece with a predetermined standard or scale. If the standard penetrator or the load is changed, the hardness number will change. Therefore certain test conditions have been standardized so that the hardness measurements can be compared when different test equipment or conditions are used. Also, the hardness number must identify the method of testing and the standard force that was used. The most common hardness testing methods are the Rockwell and Brinell tests.

The Rockwell hardness test provides a *direct reading* method to measure the depth of penetration made by pressing a diamond cone (for harder material) or a $1/16$ in. steel ball (for softer material) into the test sample to determine the relative hardness. Fig. 7-43 identifies the test application, the standard penetrator and the major load for each of the various Rockwell scales. The Rockwell "C" scale is most commonly used for typical through-hardened tool steels (such as 0-1, A-2, D-2, M-1, T-15, etc.) where hardness may vary from R/C 40 (softer) to R/C 67 (harder).

The Brinell hardness test uses a 10 mm diameter steel ball forced under a predetermined load into the softer test material. (See Fig. 7-46.) The measured diameter of the resulting penetration is

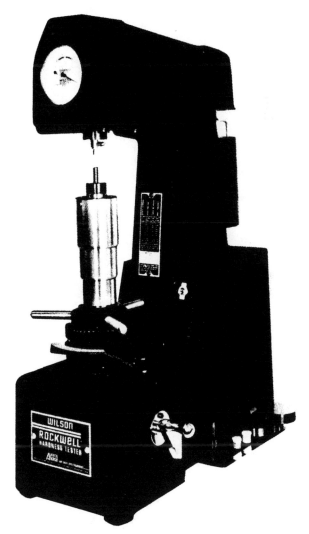

Fig. 7-44   A typical machine for performing the Rockwell hardness test. Rockwell hardness readings are taken directly from the dial on the instrument head. (Courtesy of Acco Industries Inc.)

Dia. of ball impression mm	Brinell hardness number for a load of kg			Dia. of ball impression mm	Brinell hardness number for a load of kg			Dia. of ball impression mm	Brinell hardness number for a load of kg		
	500	1500	3000		500	1500	3000		500	1500	3000
2.00	158	473	945	3.50	50.3	151	302	5.00	23.8	71.3	143
2.05	150	450	899	3.55	48.9	147	293	5.05	23.3	69.8	140
2.10	143	428	856	3.60	47.5	142	285	5.10	22.8	68.3	137
2.15	136	408	817	3.65	46.1	138	277	5.15	22.3	66.9	134
2.20	130	390	780	3.70	44.9	135	269	5.20	21.8	65.5	131
2.25	124	372	745	3.75	43.6	131	262	5.25	21.4	64.1	128
2.30	119	356	712	3.80	42.4	127	255	5.30	20.9	62.8	126
2.35	114	341	682	3.85	41.3	124	248	5.35	20.5	61.5	123
2.40	109	327	653	3.90	40.2	121	241	5.40	20.1	60.3	121
2.45	104	313	627	3.95	39.1	117	235	5.45	19.7	59.1	118
2.50	100	301	601	4.00	38.1	114	229	5.50	19.3	57.9	116
2.55	96.3	289	578	4.05	37.1	111	223	5.55	18.9	56.8	114
2.60	92.6	278	555	4.10	36.2	109	217	5.60	18.6	55.7	111
2.65	89.0	267	534	4.15	35.3	106	212	5.65	18.2	54.6	109
2.70	85.7	257	514	4.20	34.4	103	207	5.70	17.8	53.5	107
2.75	82.6	248	495	4.25	33.6	101	201	5.75	17.5	52.5	105
2.80	79.6	239	477	4.30	32.8	98.3	197	5.80	17.2	51.5	103
2.85	76.8	230	461	4.35	32.0	95.9	192	5.85	16.8	50.5	101
2.90	74.1	222	444	4.40	31.2	93.6	187	5.90	16.5	49.6	99.2
2.95	71.5	215	429	4.45	30.5	91.4	183	5.95	16.2	48.7	97.3
3.00	69.1	207	415	4.50	29.8	89.3	179	6.00	15.9	47.7	95.5
3.05	66.8	200	401	4.55	29.1	87.2	174	6.05	15.6	46.8	93.7
3.10	64.6	194	388	4.60	28.4	85.2	170	6.10	15.3	46.0	92.0
3.15	62.5	188	375	4.65	27.8	83.3	167	6.15	15.1	45.2	90.3
3.20	60.5	182	363	4.70	27.1	81.4	163	6.20	14.8	44.3	88.7
3.25	58.6	176	352	4.75	26.5	79.6	159	6.25	14.5	43.5	87.1
3.30	56.8	170	341	4.80	25.9	77.8	156	6.30	14.2	42.7	85.5
3.35	55.1	165	331	4.85	25.4	76.1	152	6.35	14.0	42.0	84.0
3.40	53.4	160	321	4.90	24.8	74.4	149	6.40	13.7	41.2	82.5
3.45	51.8	156	311	4.95	24.3	72.8	146	6.45	13.5	40.5	81.0

Fig. 7-45   Brinell hardness numbers — diameter of ball: 10 millimeters.

Fig. 7-46   One type of machine for testing Brinell hardness. The dial indicates the load but the impression in the test piece must still be measured. This tester with a special digital readout provides the BHN directly. (Courtesy of Acco Ind., Inc.)

compared to a standard chart to determine the relative Brinell hardness number (BHN). The Brinell test loading standard forces are 3000kg (160-600 BHN), 1500kg (80 to 300 BHN) and 500kg (26 to 100 BHN). The BHN for soft copper should be about 40, soft steel from 150 to 200 and hardened steel from 500 to 600 Hardened high carbon steel may reach 750 BHN.

Comparative hardness charts are available to permit hardness numbers determined under different testing standards to be compared with hardness numbers obtained by the Rockwell, Brinell and several other testing methods. (See Figs. 7-43 & 7-45.)

CHAPTER VII REVIEW

1. What are the three major types of measuring machines?

2. What are some of the advantages of measuring machines?

3. List the various mechanical, optical and electronic measuring systems incorporated in the machine shown in Fig. 7-1.

4. True or False: The multiple-axis universal measuring machine provides control of geometry, length, angles, and roundness.

5. Why are CMM's like NC machine tools?

6. List the advantages and limitations of pneumatic gaging.

7. Explain how a LVDT works.

8. What are the advantages and disadvantages of optical comparators?

9. What are the advantages of solid-state electronic measuring and gaging systems versus the older tube-type designs?

10. What three elements are common to both electric and electronic gaging systems?

Chapter VIII

Glossary

Term	Definition
Abbe's Law	— Principle that states: for maximum reliability of a measurement, the axis of the standard used must lie along the line of measurement.
Actual Size	—Measured size of a feature.
Acute Angle	—An angle smaller than a right angle.
Adjustable Gage	—Gage that indicates the amount by which a measured part deviates, plus or minus, from a standard to which the gage has been set. In most cases, the deviation is indicated directly in units of measurement but, in some cases, the gage indicates only whether or not the deviation is within a desired range.
Air Film	—The minute layer of air that separates two finely finished surfaces when wrung together.
Air Gaging	—See *Pneumatic Gaging*.
Allowance	—The prescribed difference between the Maximum Material Condition (MMC) limits of size of mating parts. If the mating parts have minimum clearance between them, the allowance is positive and is called a *clearance fit*. If the mating parts have maximum interference between them, the allowance is negative and is called an *interference fit*.
Ambient Temperature	—Surrounding temperature.
Amplification	—An increase in the output of an electric or electronic gaging system as compared to the input.

Term	*Definition*
Amplifier	—The intermediate modifying stage of an electronic gaging system that amplifies the power level of the physical quantity measured. May also incorporate other functions, such as filtering the signal and comparison of signals.
Analog Instrument	—An instrument that displays measured quantities by means of the motion of a pointer on a scale or the record of a pen moving over a chart.
Angle	—Two straight lines that meet at a point on a plane surface.
Angle Plate	—A general term for the different right-angle forms used to provide a plane perpendicular or parallel to a surface plate, against which work is rested or clamped during inspection.
Angularity	—A condition of part features in which they are positioned at an angle to each other. Specifies the condition of a surface or axis that is at some specified angle (other than 90 deg) from a datum plane or axis.
Angularity Tolerance	—A zone within which a part feature must lie, confined by two parallel planes or lines inclined at a specified angle to a datum.
Annular Plug Gage	—A shell-type plug gage in which the gaging member is in the form of a ring. The external surface is the gaging section. The central portion of the web is removed to reduce weight. Ball handles are provided for ease in handling. This construction is employed for plain and thread plug gages in the ranges above 8.010 in.
Anvil	—A precisely flat surface that serves as a stationary contact in several types of instruments used for measuring external diameters.
Area Lapping	—Selective lapping of specific portions of a surface.
Arithmetical Progression	—A sequence of numbers in which successive terms change by a constant difference.
Axis	—A straight line defined by the centers of two prescribed cross-sections; a straight line about which an object rotates.
Back-Pressure Comparator	—A pneumatic comparator utilizing a circuit in which pressure changes indicate the deviation of a dimension from a preset value.
Basic Dimension	—A theoretical (desired) feature location, size, or shape. See also *True Position Dimension.*

Basic Hole and Basic Shaft Systems — Terms used to identify which mating part is taken as a standard size. In the *basic hole system*, the minimum size of the hole is taken as the base from which all variations are made. In the *basic shaft system*, the maximum shaft size is taken as the basic size. This system is used

Term	*Definition*
	where several different fits of nominal size are required on one shaft; for example, when bearings are fitted to line shafting.
Bias	—Conscious or unconscious influencing of the measurement.
Bilateral Tolerance	—A variation permitted in both directions from a specified size, form, or location.
Black Granite	—A particular granite of exceptional density and hardness.
Bridge Circuit	—A closed network (usually with fan branches) in which a change in any branch alters the potential across the bridge.
Burrs	—Minute particles of metal projecting above the finished surface that can scratch other contacting surfaces. They should always be removed before taking measurements requiring accuracy.
Calipers	—Any instrument (either direct- or indirect-reading) whose opening between two jaws or two legs can be set to a dimension, thickness, or diameter.
Centralize or Centralizing	—Moving an instrument by feel or contact to orient its axis parallel to the line of measurement.
Chain Dimensioning	—Dimensioning in a series of steps from feature to feature on a part. Preferably called *In-Line Dimensioning.*
Chord	—A straight line joining any two points on a circle or arc.
Circle	—A closed plane curve, all of whose points are equidistant from one enclosed point, its center. Used as the standard for angular measurement.
Circumference	—The perimeter of a circle. In dimensional metrology, usually means the length of the perimeter.
Clearance	—The measured distance between two finished male and female mating parts.
Clearance	—In pneumatic gaging, the distance between the nozzle and the part.
Comparator	—Any instrument that provides the magnified or amplified difference in size between two dimensions.
Comparison Measurement	—Measurement by comparing an unknown dimension with a known dimension or standard.
Complementary Angles	—Angles which, when added, equal 90 deg.
Compound Angles	—Angles formed by the edges of triangles that lie in different planes.

Term	Definition
Concentricity	— Specifies the condition where in two or more features (cylinders, cones, spheres, hexagons) share a common axis.
Concentricity Tolerance	— A zone centered about a datum axis within which the axis, or one or more regular features, must lie.
Constraint	— Elimination of a degree of freedom.
Contact Instrument	— An instrument that depends upon physical contact with the part to make a measurement.
Contact Interference	— Condition preventing intimate contact between two plane surfaces without damage.
Contour	— The three-dimensional form developed by part feature profiles.
Contour Tolerance	— The zone created by the tolerances of part feature profiles.

Convection, Radiation and Conduction — The three ways that heat passes from one mass to another.

Term	Definition
Coordinate Dimensioning	— Rectangular dimensioning from datums based on the Cartesian coordinate system of mutually perpendicular planes.
Crowned Plate	— A surface plate whose reference surface is a portion of a sphere or very large radius.
Cumulative Error	— An error whose magnitude increases as the number of observations increases.
Cylindrical Head	— A head whose moving member travels along the axis of a cylindrical body.
Cylindrical Square	— A master right angle reference in the form of a heavy cylinder.
Cylindricity	— Specifies the condition on a revolving surface wherein all elements form a perfect cylinder.
Cylindricity Tolerance	— The specified annular zone between two concentric cylinders. Other form or positional tolerances can also be used to specify cylindricity.
Datum	— The name given to a point, line, plane, cylinder, or other geometric shape that is taken to be exact for purposes of computation, and from which the location or geometric relationship (form) of part features is established.
Datum (in Measurement)	— A physical datum from which measurements are made, usually planes in inspection equipment.

Datum (Ordinate Dimensioning) — Rectangular dimensioning in which all dimensions originate from two or more mutually perpendicular datum surfaces.

Term	*Definition*
Datum, Deformed	—A part datum feature which, in its free state, exceeds the datum tolerance.
Datum Reference Frame	—The coordinate reference system defined by three mutually perpendicular datum planes.
Datum, Restrained	—A part datum feature properly corrected to eliminate free state variations.
Datum Target	—The designated physical point or area on a part datum feature to be contacted by production and measurement equipment.
Datum Tolerance (Accuracy)	—The allowable deviation of a measurement datum from the corresponding drawing datum.
Decimal-Inch System	—System of linear measurement based on decimal division of the inch.
Degradation of Workmanship	—A generalization that no part feature is as accurate as the process or machine that produced it. Thus, the less dependent that a part feature is on previous operations, the greater the probability of its accuracy.
Degree	—In angle measurement, the 360th part of the circumference of a circle.
Degree of Freedom	—Freedom to move along a line or to rotate.
Dial Index Head	—Index head consisting of an index plate integral with a rotating spindle and a means for stopping against the plate.
Dial Indicator	—The most common of the adjustable- or deviation-type instruments. The simplest form of mechanical comparator. A mechanism for magnifying and measuring the displacement of a movable contact point, thereby measuring a dimension or variations from an established dimension.
Diameter	—A chord passing through the center of a circle or cylinder. The length of such a chord.
Difference Measurement	—Differential measurement in which one input signal is subtracted from another.
Differential Measurement	—The algebraic combination of input signals within the measuring instrument. Used to obtain concentricity, roundness, and other measurements directly.
Differential Measurement	—In pneumatic gaging, the combining of nozzles to permit measurements of features that could not be distinguished if measured separately.
Digital Instrument	—An instrument that uses or displays data in the form of digits (numerals).
Dihedral Angles	—The openings between intersecting planes.
Dimension	—Any measurable extent, such as length, width, thickness, etc.

Term	*Definition*
Dimension (Drawing)	—A numerical value expressed in appropriate units of measure, and indicated on a drawing along with lines, symbols, and notes to define the geometric size, shape, or location of a feature.
Direct Measurement	—Measuring with an instrument that incorporates a standard of length.
Discrimination	—The degree to which an instrument subdivides the standard unit of length. The finest division on such an instrument.
Displacement Measurement	—Measurement of the linear distance from the initial to the final position of an object moved from one location to another, regardless of the length of the path followed.

Dividing Heads, Indexing Heads, Index Heads — Mechanical devices that divide the circle into equal divisions.

Dynamic Measurement	—Measurement of a moving feature or changing value.
Effective Size	—See *Virtual Size.*

Electronic Measuring Instruments — Those in which signal amplification is obtained by electronic means. (In most electronic instruments, the initial pickup is mechanical.)

End Standard	—One of the two physical forms of length standards.
Error	—The difference between the measured value and the true value.
Face Angles	—The angles formed by the intersection of the edges of a solid.
Feature	—Specific characteristics or portions of a part, such as holes, slots, profiles, etc.
Feel	—The perception by the user of physical contact between a part and an instrument.
Film	—A substance separating wrung surfaces. May be air and/or oil.
Finished Size	—Actual measured size.
FIR	—Full indicator reading.
Fit	—The term commonly used to describe the range of tightness or looseness that results from applying a specific combination of allowances and clearances to the design of mating parts.
Fixed-Size Gage	—A gage that is finished to an exact size and cannot be adjusted in any manner. Fixed-size gages are designed to gage only one dimension, and indicate only whether or not the dimension is larger or smaller than a previously established standard.

Term	Definition
Flange	—The external portion of a ring gage that is reduced in section to reduce weight.
Flatness	—The measure of deviation from a reference plane.
Flatness Tolerance	—*Flatness* specifies that all points of an actual surface must lie in a zone between two parallel planes that are a distance apart equal to the specified tolerance.
Flats	—Small surface plates, usually of high accuracy.
Flow-Rate Comparator	—Pneumatic comparator utilizing a circuit in which air flow rate changes result from a nozzle restriction.
Flow Tube	—A tapered vertical tube with an air float and a fluid column used as the read-out stage of a pneumatic comparator.
Form Tolerance	—A tolerance zone that controls part feature geometry.
Free State Variation	—The amount that a part distorts following the removal of an external force applied during manufacture, inspection, or assembly.
Frictionless Head	—A measuring head using reed suspension of the moving members to eliminate mechanical friction.
Functional Gage	—A gage that simulates the most critical conformation of the mating part, and "receives" the part being gaged. Used for inspection or rejection of parts. Also called a *Receiving Gage*.
Gage Block Grades	—The accuracy grades of gage blocks established by Federal Government specifications, and expanded by manufacturers' specifications.
Gage Block Holders	—The hardware that secures end standards and gage blocks into one unit.
Gage Blocks	—The mass-produced end standards that combine arithmetically to form usable length combinations. Used as the physical industrial standards of precise linear measurement in most manufacturing processes.
Gage Pin	—Standard pins commercially available in 0.0001 in. increments.
Gages	—Comparison-type measuring instruments used for production measuring. They are used to measure both linear and angular dimensions, and are either of the fixed-size or adjustable type.
Gaging	—The process of determining whether or not a dimension of a part is larger or smaller than an established standard, or standards, by direct or indirect comparison. Also a single-purpose measurement used to sort parts or objects into size categories.

Term	Definition
GO Gage	—A plug or ring gage that represents maximum metal conditions (MMC), and which passes all parts within size limits.
Granite	—A hard, igneous, natural stone used for industrial purposes.
Heat Sink	—A surface having rapid heat transfer capability on which objects may be placed to rapidly reach ambient (room) temperature.
Inch-Pound System	—System of measurement based on the use of the inch, pound, and second, also called the *English* or *Customary System*.
Index Head	—A plate having circles of equally-spaced holes into which a stop pin can be inserted.
Indicating Gage	—One that shows the amount of variation in size from the basic dimension.
Indicator Range	—Useful portion of total travel.
Indicator Stand	—Self-supporting device that provides a reference point for an indicator.
Indirect Measurement	—Measuring with an instrument that does not contain graduations, but is used to transfer the size of the dimension being measured to a direct-reading scale, thereby obtaining the desired size information in an indirect manner.
Inspection	—Examination by measurement, gaging, or other means to verify a part's or an object's compliance with predetermined standards.
Inspection Error	—Total instrument, environment, and inspector error combined.
Inspection Gages	—Gages used by a manufacturer or a purchaser in acceptance of a part or product. A gagemaker's tolerance is always applied, and a wear allowance, where applicable, is included in their design.
Interference	—The interaction between energy pulses when two rays are brought together (see Interferometry).
Interferometry	—The use of the interference phenomena of light waves for measurement.
International Inch	—The inch standard of major inch-pound system countries, equal to 25.4mm.
Interpolation	—The arbitrary selection of the nearest graduation when a measurement lies between graduations. The observational equivalent to rounding off in computation.

Term	*Definition*
Krypton-86	—The gas which, when electrically excited, emits a very stable wavelength of light that is used as the basis for the international standard of length.
Lapping	—Abrasive stock removal process using loose abrasive particles to produce a very smooth, flat finish on metal.
Layout	—Preparation for machining or assembly.
Least Material Condition (LMC)	—A modifier applied to parts that require precise positioning so that they will assemble properly (abbreviated LMC). An LMC feature is derived from its toleranced dimensions so that it contains the least amount of material with respect to any portion of the feature that will affect a position or form tolerance. For a hole, LMC represents the high dimensional limit. For a shaft outside diameter, LMC represents the low dimensional limit.
Level Comparator	—A length comparator using a level as the transducer to convert length changes into linear values.
Level, Spirit	—Instrument that establishes a horizontal reference by means of gravity.
Limit	—Maximum or minimum stated value.
Limit Dimensioning	—Maximum and minimum dimensions are specified.
Limit Gage	—A gage that represents a limiting (maximum or minimum) size within which the work will be acceptable.
Limits of Size	—The name given to the extreme maximum and minimum sizes specified by a toleranced dimension.

Linear-Variable Differential Transformer — The most common pickup element in electronic instruments. Abbreviated LVDT.

Line Standards	—One of the two physical forms of length standards.
Logarithmic Functions	—Tables of natural functions expressed as logarithms of the decimal values.
Logarithms	—Generally used to mean "common logarithms." These are the exponents to which the number 10 must be raised to equal the desired number. For example, the logarithm of 100 is 2, because $10^2 = 100$. The logarithm of 23 is 1.36173, because $10^{1.36173} = 23$.
Magnification	—The process of enlarging the input signal of mechanical or pneumatic systems without increasing its power.

Term	Definition
Manipulative Error	—Human error caused by incorrect handling of the part and/or instrument.
Master Disk	—A cylinder provided with insulating grips, used to set comparators, snap gages, and other types of gages.
Master Gages	—Made to their basic dimensions as accurately as possible, and used for reference, such as to check or set inspection or working gages.
Mastering	—The use of setting standards for calibration of pneumatic comparators.
Maximum Material Condition (MMC)	—A modifier that specifies the maximum limit of the size of an external feature, or the minimum limit of the size of an internal feature; for example: minimum hole diameter or maximum shaft diameter. Abbreviated MMC, it is the most critical specified interchangeable size of a part feature. An MMC feature is derived from its toleranced dimensions so that it contains the maximum amount of material with respect to any portion of the feature that will affect a form or positional tolerance.
Maximum Material Limit	—The limit of size that provides the maximum amount of material for a part. It is usually the maximum limit of size of an external dimension, or the minimum limit of size of an internal dimension.
Measurement	—The determination of a dimension of a part through the use of some type of instrument that permits the magnitude of the dimension to be determined, either directly or indirectly, in terms of scalar units.
Mechanical Comparator	—A contact comparator in which mechanical movement is magnified, usually by a rack, pinion, and pointer, or by a parallelogram arrangement.
Metrology Laboratory	—A laboratory where standards are calibrated. May be a department within a company, or an outside service.
Millionths	—Measurements carried to six decimal places.
Minimum Material Limit	—The limit of size that provides the minimum amount of material for a part. It is usually the minimum limit of size of an external dimension, or the maximum limit of size of an internal dimension.
Minute	—One 60th part of a degree. One 21,600th part of a circle.
Natural Functions	—Tables of trigonometric functions divided into decimals.
Nominal Size	—That size exactly half-way between the limits of size. Approximate size used for the purpose of general identification.
NOT-GO	—Interaction between a gage and a part that shows that the part is out-of-tolerance. Sometimes used as NO-GO.

Term	*Definition*
NOT-GO Gage	—A plug or ring gage that represents the least material conditon (LMC), and which passes all parts within size limits.
Nozzle, Orifice, Jet	—In reference to pneumatic comparators, the exit openings at the gaging element.
Observational Error	—Human error that occurs while reading a measurement.
Obtuse Angle	—An angle larger than a right angle.
Parallax	—Change in the apparent relative positions of objects due to the changed position of observer. Source of parallax error.
Parallax Error	—Error in reading an instrument employing a scale and pointer, because the observer's eye and pointer are not in a line perpendicular to the plane of the scale.
Parallelism	—Specifies the condition of a surface or axis that is equidistant at all points from a datum plane or axis.
Parallelism Tolerance	—A zone, limited by two planes or straight lines parallel to a datum, within which an axis or entire surface of a part must lie.
Parallelogram	—A four-sided closed figure whose opposite sides are parallel.
Perpendicularity	—Specifies the condition of a surface, median plane, or axis that is at a 90 deg angle to a datum plane or axis. In surface plate work, perpendicularity is generally synonymous to vertical.
Pi (π)	—Ratio of the circumference to the diameter of a circle (3.1415926536+).
Pickup Head, Gage Head, Head	—The detector-transducer stage of an electronic measuring system that converts a length change into its electrical analog.
Plain Adjustable Snap Gage	—A complete external-caliper gage used for size control of plain external dimensions. It consists of an open frame and two jaws, in both of which gaging members are provided. One or more pairs of gaging members can be set and locked to any predetermined size within the range of adjustment.
Plain Cylindrical Plug Gage	—A complete unthreaded internal gage consisting of a handle and a gaging member. The GO and NOT-GO gaging sections are secured to one or both ends of the handle.
Plain Ring Gage	—An unthreaded external gage of circular form used for the size control of external diameters. In the smaller sizes, it consists of a gage body into which a bushing is pressed that is accurately finished to size for gaging purposes.

Term	*Definition*
Plain Solid Snap Gage	—A complete external-caliper gage used for size control of plain external dimensions. It consists of an open frame and jaws, the latter holding gaging members in the form of fixed, parallel, non-adjustable anvils.
Platen	—A term sometimes used for *anvil* or *reference surface.*
Plate Work	—General term for measurements made from a surface plate.
Plug Gage	—A gage whose outside measuring surfaces are designed to test the size and/or contour of a hole or cavity. A plug gage may be straight or tapered, plain or threaded, and of any cross-sectional shape.
Pneumatic Comparator	—The instrument used to compare lengths, areas, or finishes by means of pneumatic metrology.
Pneumatic Gaging	—Measurement by means of pneumatic metrology. Sometimes called *Air Gaging.*
Pneumatic Metrology	—Measurement in which signal magnification is achieved by a circuit containing air or other gases.
Position	—Specifies the true position, or theoretically-exact location of a point, line or plane (usually the center) of a feature in relation to a datum reference or other feature. Also called *True Position.*
Power	—The ratio of the output to the input in a measuring system.
Power Amplification	—The amplification of the loading as well as the amplitude of the input signal in an electronic measuring system.
Probe Head	—A pickup head whose moving member is a lever arm that can be inserted into openings too small for the head itself.
Profile	—An outline of a cross-section of a part feature.
Profile of a Line	—Specifies the condition permitting a uniform amount of profile variation along a line element of a feature, either unilaterally or bilaterally.
Profile of a Surface	—Specifies the condition permitting a uniform amount of profile variation on a surface, either unilaterally or bilaterally.
Profile Tolerance	—A zone within which the profile of a part feature must lie.
Progressive Cylindrical Plug Gage	— A complete internal gage consisting of a handle and a gaging member in which the GO and NOT-GO gaging sections are combined in a single unit secured to one end of the handle.
Protractor	—A direct-reading measuring instrument for angles.

Term	Definition
Radius	—A line from the center to the circumference of a circle, equal to one-half of the diameter.
Readability	—The relative ease with which a measurement can be distinguished on a scaled instrument.
Read-out	—The data that a measuring system presents to the observer.
Receiver Gage	—See *Functional Gage.*
Reed-Type Instrument	—An instrument in which spring suspension is substituted for shaft bearings, knife edges, and other mechanical friction-producing suspensions.
Reference Plane (Datum Plane)	— Plane in which reference points lie perpendicular to the line of measurement. Also called *Datum Plane.*
Reflectivity	—Mirror-like quality having little relation to surface finish or flatness.
Regardless of Feature Size	—A modifier that means that the tolerances cannot vary. Abbreviated RFS, it indicates that the tolerances of form or position of the feature are fixed and must not be exceeded, regardless of the finished size of the feature. This modifier is used, for example, on a drawing for a part designed to rotate and which must be balanced. As applied to datum features, the actual axis of a part datum feature that must be used for measurement, regardless of its finished size (within limits).
Reliable Measurement	—Measurement in which the probability of error is small.
Repeatability	—The variation among several measurements taken with one instrument on one part feature. A measure of precision, not of accuracy.
Reversible or Trilock Plug Gage	— A plug gage in which three wedge-shaped locking prongs on the handle are forced into corresponding locking grooves in the gaging member by means of a single through-screw, thus providing a self-centering support with a positive lock.
Ring Gage	—A gage whose inside measuring surfaces are circular in form. They may be either cylindrical or conical, plain or threaded.
Right Angle	—One-fourth part of a circle, or 90 deg.
Right Triangle	—A triangle in which one angle is a right angle.
Rocking	—Pivoting an instrument around one or the other of its contact points.
Roundness	—Specifies the condition on a revolving surface (cylinder, cone, or sphere) wherein all points on the surface intersected by any plane are equidistant from the axis.

Term	*Definition*
Roundness Tolerance	—A zone limited by two concentric circles within which a section of a part must lie.
Runout	—Specifies the deviation from the desired form of the revolving surface of a part as detected during full rotation of the part on a datum axis when using a dial indicator or similar measuring device.
Scale	—The graduations on a rule or other graduated measuring instruments.
Second	—One 60th part of a minute. One 3600th part of a degree. One 1,296,000th part of a circle.
Sensitivity	—Minimum input signal that produces a discernible output.
Serial Measurements	—An interconnected series of measurements.
Serrated Anvil	—An anvil having closely-spaced grooves to reduce surface area. Used to minimize the effect of air film.
Sexagesimal System	—A measurement system based on the number 60 such as that used for angle and circular measurement.
Sine Bar	—A bar to which two identical cylinders are attached with a known separation and a known relation to the reference surface of the bar. The bar becomes the hypotenuse of a triangle used for angle measurement.
Sine Bar Constants	—Table of sine and angle relationships for angle settings with sine devices.
Sine Blocks	—Wide sine bars.
Sine Plates	—Still wider sine bars.
Sine Tables	—Sine devices incorporated into machines or mechanisms.
Snap Gage	—A fixed caliper-gage arranged with inside measuring surfaces used for gaging diameters, lengths, thicknesses, or widths.
Snap Gage Pin	—The straight, unflanged adjustable gaging member of an adjustable snap gage.
Sorting	—Measurement that separates parts into lots rather than provides specific dimensional information.
Spline Plug Gage	—A plug gage having a series of projecting keys equally spaced about the periphery, which fit into the spline ways to be gaged.
Square	—The condition of being at a right angle to a line or plane. Also, a right angle in physical form.
Square Level	—A level and square combined.

Term	*Definition*
Stability	—The inherent ability of a material to retain its size over a period of time.

Stack of Gage Blocks, Combination of Gage Blocks — Two or more gage blocks wrung together to form a particular length dimension.

Steel Rule	—The most common direct-reading measuring instrument used as the standard with which the unknown dimension is compared to a graduated scale.
Straightness	—Specifies that any longitudinal element of a cylindrical part must lie between two parallel lines that are a distance apart equal to the specified tolerance.
Supplementary Angles	—Angles which, when added, equal 180 deg.
Surface Plate	—A horizontal reference plane of sufficient strength and rigidity to support measuring operations.
Surface Texture	—The variations or changes from a nominal surface which form a pattern of that surface. Includes characteristics called roughness, waviness, lay and flaw. (ASA standard B46.1-1962)
Symmetry	—Specifies the condition wherein either a part or feature has the same size and contour on both opposing sides of its median plane, or in which a feature shares a common plane with a datum plane.
Symmetry Tolerance	—A positional tolerance controlling symmetry.
Taperlock Plug Gage	—A term describing a particular gage construction in which the gaging member has a tapered shank that is forced into a tapered hole in the handle.
Taper Plug Gage	—An internal gage in the form of a frustum of a cone having diameter, taper, and length suitable for the internal gaging of taper dimensions in accordance with the specifications of the product. An extended portion may be provided for checking a tang slot when specified.
Taper Ring Gage	—An external gage whose internal contour conforms to the frustum of a cone having diameter, taper, and length suitable for the gaging of external taper dimensions in accordance with the specifications of the product. An extended portion may be provided for checking a driving tang when specified.
Ten-to-One Rule	—A general rule in gaging that states that a gage must be ten times more accurate than the dimension being checked.
Test Indicator	—A mechanical comparator providing only a two-value signal (too large and OK, yes and no, on-size and out-of-size).
Thousandths	—Measurements carried out to three decimal places.

Term	*Definition*
Thread Plug Gage	—A complete internal thread gage, either single- or double-ended, consisting of a handle and threaded gaging member or members, with suitable locking means.
Thread Ring Gage	—An external thread gage used to control the size of threaded work. It may be of solid design, or provided with a means for adjustment—for expanding, contracting, and locking the thread ring gage during manufacturing or resizing processes. The adjusting device consists of an adjusting screw, a locking screw, and a sleeve.
Thread Snap Gages	—Conical points, or serrated or threaded blades, plates, or cylinders that are adjustably-mounted in a snap gage frame.
TIR	—Total indicator reading.
Tolerance	—Total amount that a specific dimension may vary between its limits.
Toolmaker's Flats	—Flats made from steel, granite or other opaque material.
Traceability	—Documentation to establish that standards are known in relation to successively higher standards.
Transfer of Measurement	—Operation in which an indirect-reading instrument is used to transfer the size of the dimension being measured to a direct-reading scale or standard.
Triangle	—Geometric figure formed by three lines intersecting in pairs at three points. This three-sided closed figure forms three angles totaling 180 deg.
Trigonometric Functions	—The six ratios among pairs of right triangle sides. Useful in solving right angle relationships. Also called *Trigonometric Ratios*.
Trigonometry	—The branch of mathematics dealing with the relationships among the sides of triangles to the angles formed by them.
Trilock Plug Gage	—A plug in which three wedge-shaped locking prongs on the end of the handle are engaged with corresponding locking grooves in the end of the gaging member by means of a single through-screw, thus providing a self-centering support with a positive non-rotating lock.
True Position	—See *Position*.
True Position Dimension	—The theoretically exact location of a part feature established by basic dimensions. See *Basic Dimension*.
Unilateral Tolerance	—A variation permitted in only one direction from a specified size, form, or location.
Unit of Length	—Unit of measure recognized as a standard of length.

Term	Definition
Universal Bevel Protractor	—Precision protractor with an adjustable reference surface and a vernier scale fastened to a turret scale used to measure angles.
Universal Index Head	—An index head with differential gearing and usually a trunion to tilt the axis of the spindle.
Vernier Caliper	—A slide caliper that incorporates a vernier scale to achieve a discrimination of 0.001 in.
Vernier Depth Gage	—A depth gage that incorporates a vernier scale to achieve a discrimination of 0.001 in.
Vernier Height Gage	—Essentially a vernier caliper whose reference surface is a horizontal base. Used primarily for height measurement.
Vernier Instrument	—An instrument incorporating a short auxiliary scale that slides along the main instrument scale to permit accurate fractional reading of the least division of the main scale.
Vernier Scale	—An amplifying scale that has one division more in a given length than the main scale.
Vertex	—The intersection of two straight lines forming an angle.
Virtual Size	—The effective assembly size of a part feature. The largest cylinder perpendicular to a datum surface that will pass through a hole, or the smallest cylinder perpendicular to a datum surface that will pass over a pin or stud.
Wear Blocks	—Steel or tungsten carbide blocks, made in 0.050 or 0.100 in. lengths, used as the end blocks of gage block combinations to protect the inside blocks from wear.
Wear-Limit Gage	—A gage used to determine when a limit gage or functional gage has worn to the maximum permitted.
Wide-Range Divider	—A means of compounding index plates for very high amplification.
Wire-Type Plug Gage	—A plug gage consisting of a gaging member of straight cylindrical section throughout its length, held in a collet-type handle.
Working Flats	—Flats used for most routine inspection.
Working Gages	—Used for inspection of parts during production. For the product to be within the limits of inspection gages, working gages usually have dimensional limits (resulting from gage tolerances and wear allowances) that are slightly farther from the specified limits than inspection gages.
Working Surface	—The finished surface or surfaces of a flat or surface plate.

Term	*Definition*
Wringing or Wrung Surfaces	—The adhesion between almost perfectly flat surfaces when brought into intimate contact by means of sliding pressure.
Wringing Interval	—The separation between two wrung surfaces.
Zero Setting	—Bringing the zero position of an instrument into correspondence with a reference of the measurement.

APPENDIX

Conversion Table — Fractions, Decimals, and Millimeters

inches fractions	decimals	mm		inches fractions	decimals	mm
—	.0004	.01		—	.413	10.5
—	.004	.10		27/64	.422	10.716
—	.01	.25		—	.4331	11.
1/64	.0156	.397		7/16	.438	11.113
—	.0197	.50		29/64	.453	11.509
—	.0295	.75		15/32	.469	11.906
1/32	.03125	.794		—	.4724	12.
—	.0394	1.		31/64	.484	12.303
3/64	.0469	1.191		—	.492	12.5
—	.059	1.5		1/2	.500	12.700
1/16	.062	1.588		—	.5118	13.
5/64	.0781	1.984		33/64	.5156	13.097
—	.0787	2.		17/32	.531	13.494
3/32	.094	2.381		35/64	.547	13.891
—	.0984	2.5		—	.5512	14.
7/64	.109	2.778		9/16	.563	14.288
—	.1181	3.		—	.571	14.5
1/8	.125	3.175		37/64	.578	14.684
—	.1378	3.5		—	.5906	15.
9/64	.141	3.572		19/32	.594	15.081
5/32	.156	3.969		39/64	.609	15.478
—	.1575	4.		5/8	.625	15.875
11/64	.172	4.366		—	.6299	16.
—	.177	4.5		41/64	.6406	16.272
3/16	.1875	4.763		—	.6496	16.5
—	.1969	5.		21/32	.656	16.669
13/64	.203	5.159		—	.6693	17.
—	.2165	5.5		43/64	.672	17.066
7/32	.219	5.556		11/16	.6875	17.463
15/64	.234	5.953		45/64	.703	17.859
—	.2362	6.		—	.7087	18.
1/4	.250	6.350		23/32	.719	18.256
—	.2559	6.5		—	.7283	18.5
17/64	.2656	6.747		47/64	.734	18.653
—	.2756	7.		—	.7480	19.
9/32	.281	7.144		3/4	.750	19.050
—	.2953	7.5		49/64	.7656	19.447
19/64	.297	7.541		25/32	.781	19.844
5/16	.312	7.938		—	.7874	20.
—	.315	8.		51/64	.797	20.241
21/64	.328	8.334		13/16	.8125	20.638
—	.335	8.5		—	.8268	21.
11/32	.344	8.731		53/64	.828	21.034
—	.3543	9.		27/32	.844	21.431
23/64	.359	9.128		55/64	.859	21.828
—	.374	9.5		—	.8661	22.
3/8	.375	9.525		7/8	.875	22.225
25/64	.391	9.922		57/64	.8906	22.622
—	.3937	10.		—	.9055	23.
13/32	.406	10.319		29/32	.9062	23.019

| inches | | mm |
fractions	decimals	
59/64	.922	23.416
15/16	.9375	23.813
—	.9449	24.
61/64	.953	24.209
31/32	.969	24.606
—	.9843	25.
63/64	.9844	25.003
1	1.000	25.400
—	1.0236	26.
1 1/32	1.0312	26.194
1 1/16	1.062	26.988
—	1.063	27.
1 3/32	1.094	27.781
—	1.1024	28.
1 1/8	1.125	28.575
—	1.1417	29.
1 5/32	1.156	29.369
—	1.1811	30.
1 3/16	1.1875	30.163
1 7/32	1.219	30.956
—	1.2205	31.
1 1/4	1.250	31.750
—	1.2598	32.
1 9/32	1.281	32.544
—	1.2992	33.
1 5/16	1.312	33.338
—	1.3386	34.
1 11/32	1.344	34.131
1 3/8	1.375	34.925
—	1.3779	35.
1 13/32	1.406	35.719
—	1.4173	36.
1 7/16	1.438	36.513
—	1.4567	37.
1 15/32	1.469	37.306
—	1.4961	38.
1 1/2	1.500	38.100
1 17/32	1.531	38.894
—	1.5354	39.
1 9/16	1.562	39.688
—	1.5748	40.
1 19/32	1.594	40.481
—	1.6142	41.
1 5/8	1.625	41.275
—	1.6535	42.
1 21/32	1.6562	42.069
1 11/16	1.6875	42.863
—	1.6929	43.
1 23/32	1.719	43.656
—	1.7323	44.
1 3/4	1.750	44.450
—	1.7717	45.
1 25/32	1.781	45.244
—	1.8110	46.
1 13/16	1.8125	46.038

| inches | | mm |
fractions	decimals	
1 27/32	1.844	46.831
—	1.8504	47
1 7/8	1.875	47.625
—	1.8898	48.
1 29/32	1.9062	48.419
—	1.9291	49.
1 15/16	1.9375	49.213
—	1.9685	50.
1 31/32	1.969	50.006
2	2.000	50.800
—	2.0079	51.
2 1/32	2.03125	51.594
—	2.0472	52.
2 1/16	2.062	52.388
—	2.0866	53.
2 3/32	2.094	53.181
2 1/8	2.125	53.975
—	2.126	54.
2 5/32	2.156	54.769
—	2.165	55.
2 3/16	2.1875	55.563
—	2.2047	56.
2 7/32	2.219	56.356
—	2.244	57.
2 1/4	2.250	57.150
2 9/32	2.281	57.944
—	2.2835	58.
2 5/16	2.312	58.738
—	2.3228	59.
2 11/32	2.344	59.531
—	2.3622	60.
2 3/8	2.375	60.325
—	2.4016	61.
2 13/32	2.406	61.119
2 7/16	2.438	61.913
—	2.4409	62.
2 15/32	2.469	62.706
—	2.4803	63.
2 1/2	2.500	63.500
—	2.5197	64.
2 17/32	2.531	64.294
—	2.559	65.
2 9/16	2.562	65.088
2 19/32	2.594	65.881
—	2.5984	66.
2 5/8	2.625	66.675
—	2.638	67.
2 21/32	2.656	67.469
—	2.6772	68.
2 11/16	2.6875	68.263
—	2.7165	69.
2 23/32	2.719	69.056
2 3/4	2.750	69.850
—	2.7559	70.
2 25/32	2.781	70.6439

inches fractions	inches decimals	mm
—	2.7953	71.
2 13/16	2.8125	71.4376
—	2.8346	72.
2 27/32	2.844	72.2314
—	2.8740	73.
2 7/8	2.875	73.025
2 29/32	2.9062	73.819
—	2.9134	74.
2 15/16	2.9375	74.613
—	2.9527	75.
2 31/32	2.969	75.406
—	2.9921	76.
3	3.000	76.200
3 1/32	3.0312	76.994
—	3.0315	77.
3 1/16	3.062	77.788
—	3.0709	78.
3 3/32	3.094	78.581
—	3.1102	79.
3 1/8	3.125	79.375
—	3.1496	80.
3 5/32	3.156	80.169
3 3/16	3.1875	80.963
—	3.1890	81.
3 7/32	3.219	81.756
—	3.2283	82.
3 1/4	3.250	82.550
—	3.2677	83.
3 9/32	3.281	83.344
—	3.3071	84.
3 5/16	3.312	84.1377
3 11/32	3.344	84.9314
—	3.3464	85.
3 3/8	3.375	85.725
—	3.3858	86.
3 13/32	3.406	86.519
—	3.4252	87.
3 7/16	3.438	87.313
—	3.4646	88.
3 15/32	3.469	88.106
3 1/2	3.500	88.900
—	3.5039	89.
3 17/32	3.531	89.694
—	3.5433	90.
3 9/16	3.562	90.4877
—	3.5827	91.
3 19/32	3.594	91.281
—	3.622	92.
3 5/8	3.625	92.075
3 21/32	3.656	92.869
—	3.6614	93.
3 11/16	3.6875	93.663
—	3.7008	94.
3 23/32	3.719	94.456
—	3.7401	95.

inches fractions	inches decimals	mm
3 3/4	3.750	95.250
—	3.7795	96.
3 25/32	3.781	96.044
3 13/16	3.8125	96.838
—	3.8189	97.
3 27/32	3.844	97.631
—	3.8583	98.
3 7/8	3.875	98.425
—	3.8976	99.
3 29/32	3.9062	99.219
—	3.9370	100.
3 15/16	3.9375	100.013
3 31/32	3.969	100.806
—	3.9764	101.
4	4.000	101.600
4 1/16	4.062	103.188
4 1/8	4.125	104.775
—	4.1338	105.
4 3/16	4.1875	106.363
4 1/4	4.250	107.950
4 5/16	4.312	109.538
—	4.3307	110.
4 3/8	4.375	111.125
4 7/16	4.438	112.713
4 1/2	4.500	114.300
—	4.5275	115.
4 9/16	4.562	115.888
4 5/8	4.625	117.475
4 11/16	4.6875	119.063
—	4.7244	120.
4 3/4	4.750	120.650
4 13/16	4.8125	122.238
4 7/8	4.875	123.825
—	4.9212	125.
4 15/16	4.9375	125.413
5	5.000	127.000
—	5.1181	130.
5 1/4	5.250	133.350
5 1/2	5.500	139.700
—	5.5118	140.
5 3/4	5.750	146.050
—	5.9055	150.
6	6.000	152.400
6 1/4	6.250	158.750
—	6.2992	160.
6 1/2	6.500	165.100
—	6.6929	170.
6 3/4	6.750	171.450
7	7.000	177.800
—	7.0866	180.
—	7.4803	190.
7 1/2	7.500	190.500
—	7.8740	200.
8	8.000	203.200
—	8.2677	210.

inches		mm
fractions	decimals	
8 1/2	8.500	215.900
—	8.6614	220.
9	9.000	228.600
—	9.0551	230.
—	9.4488	240.
9 1/2	9.500	241.300
—	9.8425	250.
10	10.000	254.001
—	10.2362	260.
—	10.6299	270.
11	11.000	279.401
—	11.0236	280.
—	11.4173	290.
—	11.8110	300.

inches		mm
fractions	decimals	
12	12.000	304.801
13	13.000	330.201
—	13.7795	350.
14	14.000	355.601
15	15.000	381.001
—	15.7480	400.
16	16.000	406.401
17	17.000	431.801
—	17.7165	450.
18	18.000	457.201
19	19.000	482.601
—	19.6850	500.
20	20.000	508.001

Squares, Square Roots, Cubes, and Cube Roots

No.	Square	Cube	Square Root	Cube Root	No.	Square	Cube	Square Root	Cube Root
1	1	1	1.0000	1.0000	46	2116	97336	6.7823	3.5830
2	4	8	1.4142	1.2599	47	2209	103823	6.8557	3.6088
3	9	27	1.7321	1.4422	48	2304	110592	6.9282	3.6342
4	16	64	2.0000	1.5874	49	2401	117649	7.0000	3.6593
5	25	125	2.2361	1.7100	50	2500	125000	7.0711	3.6840
6	36	216	2.4495	1.8171	51	2601	132651	7.1414	3.7084
7	49	343	2.6458	1.9129	52	2704	140608	7.2111	3.7325
8	64	512	2.8284	2.0000	53	2809	148877	7.2801	3.7563
9	81	729	3.0000	2.0801	54	2916	157464	7.3485	3.7798
10	100	1000	3.1623	2.1544	55	3025	166375	7.4162	3.8030
11	121	1331	3.3166	2.2240	56	3136	175616	7.4833	3.8259
12	144	1728	3.4641	2.2894	57	3249	185193	7.5498	3.8485
13	169	2197	3.6056	2.3513	58	3364	195112	7.6158	3.8709
14	196	2744	3.7417	2.4101	59	3481	205379	7.6811	3.8930
15	225	3375	3.8730	2.4662	60	3600	216000	7.7460	3.9149
16	256	4096	4.0000	2.5198	61	3721	226981	7.8102	3.9365
17	289	4913	4.1231	2.5713	62	3844	238328	7.8740	3.9579
18	324	5832	4.2426	2.6207	63	3969	250047	7.9373	3.9791
19	361	6859	4.3589	2.6684	64	4096	262144	8.0000	4.0000
20	400	8000	4.4721	2.7144	65	4225	274625	8.0623	4.0207
21	441	9261	4.5826	2.7589	66	4356	287496	8.1240	4.0412
22	484	10648	4.6904	2.8020	67	4489	300763	8.1854	4.0615
23	529	12167	4.7958	2.8439	68	4624	314432	8.2462	4.0817
24	576	13824	4.8990	2.8845	69	4761	328509	8.3066	4.1016
25	625	15625	5.0000	2.9240	70	4900	343000	8.3666	4.1213
26	676	17576	5.0990	2.9625	71	5041	357911	8.4261	4.1408
27	729	19683	5.1962	3.0000	72	5184	373248	8.4853	4.1602
28	784	21952	5.2915	3.0366	73	5329	389017	8.5440	4.1793
29	841	24389	5.3852	3.0723	74	5476	405224	8.6023	4.1983
30	900	27000	5.4772	3.1072	75	5625	421875	8.6603	4.2172
31	961	29791	5.5678	3.1414	76	5776	438976	8.7178	4.2358
32	1024	32768	5.6569	3.1748	77	5929	456533	8.7750	4.2543
33	1089	35937	5.7446	3.2075	78	6084	474552	8.8318	4.2727
34	1156	39304	5.8310	3.2396	79	6241	493039	8.8882	4.2908
35	1225	42875	5.9161	3.2711	80	6400	512000	8.9443	4.3089
36	1296	46656	6.0000	3.3019	81	6561	531441	9.0000	4.3267
37	1369	50653	6.0828	3.3322	82	6724	551368	9.0554	4.3445
38	1444	54872	6.1644	3.3620	83	6889	571787	9.1104	4.3621
39	1521	59319	6.2450	3.3912	84	7056	592704	9.1652	4.3795
40	1600	64000	6.3246	3.4200	85	7225	614125	9.2195	4.3968
41	1681	68921	6.4031	3.4482	86	7396	636056	9.2736	4.4140
42	1764	74088	6.4807	3.4760	87	7569	658503	9.3274	4.4310
43	1849	79507	6.5574	3.5034	88	7744	681472	9.3808	4.4480
44	1936	85184	6.6332	3.5303	89	7921	704969	9.4340	4.4647
45	2025	91125	6.7082	3.5569	90	8100	729000	9.4868	4.4814

Squares, Square Roots, Cubes, and Cube Roots (cont.)

No.	Square	Cube	Square Root	Cube Root
91	8281	753571	9.5394	4.4979
92	8464	778688	9.5917	4.5144
93	8649	804357	9.6457	4.5307
94	8836	830584	9.6954	4.5468
95	9025	857375	9.7468	4.5629
96	9216	884736	9.7980	4.5789
97	9409	912673	9.8489	4.5947
98	9604	941192	9.8995	4.6104
99	9801	970299	9.9499	4.6261
100	10000	1000000	10.0000	4.6416
101	10201	1030301	10.0499	4.6570
102	10404	1061208	10.0995	4.6723
103	10609	1092727	10.1489	4.6875
104	10816	1124864	10.1980	4.7027
105	11025	1157625	10.2470	4.7177
106	11236	1191016	10.2956	4.7326
107	11449	1225043	10.3441	4.7475
108	11664	1259712	10.3923	4.7622
109	11881	1295029	10.4403	4.7769
110	12100	1331000	10.4881	4.7914
111	12321	1367631	10.5357	4.8059
112	12544	1404928	10.5830	4.8203
113	12769	1442897	10.6301	4.8346
114	12996	1481544	10.6771	4.8488
115	13225	1520875	10.7238	4.8629
116	13456	1560896	10.7703	4.8770
117	13689	1601613	10.8167	4.8910
118	13924	1643032	10.8628	4.9049
119	14161	1685159	10.9087	4.9187
120	14400	1728000	10.9545	4.9324
121	14641	1771561	11.0000	4.9461
122	14884	1815848	11.0454	4.9597
123	15129	1860867	11.0905	4.9732
124	15376	1906624	11.1355	4.9866
125	15625	1953125	11.1803	5.0000
126	15876	2000376	11.2250	5.0133
127	16129	2048383	11.2694	5.0265
128	16384	2097152	11.3137	5.0397
129	16641	2146689	11.3578	5.0528
130	16900	2197000	11.4018	5.0653
131	17161	2248091	11.4455	5.0788
132	17424	2299968	11.4891	5.0916
133	17689	2352637	11.5326	5.1045
134	17956	2406104	11.5758	5.1172

I N D E X